KiDS

# BIG Quiz Book

## 1001 brain busting trivia questions

# Contents

NATIONAL GEOGRAPHIC KiDS

# BIG Quiz Book

Published by Collins
An imprint of HarperCollins Publi
Westerhill Road
Bishopbriggs
Glasgow G64 2QT
www.harpercollins.co.uk

In association with National Geographic Partners, LLC



First published 2020



ISBN 978-0-00-840896-1

10 9 8 7 6 5 4 3 2 1



A catalogue record for this book is available from the British Library

Printed and bound in Slovenia by GPS Group.

If you would like to comment on any aspect of this book, please contact us at the above address or online.
natgeokidsbooks.co.uk
collins.reference@harpercollins.co.uk

Paper from responsible sources

Image credits
P92 Angler fish image © Helmut Corneli/Alamy Stock Photo
All other images © Shutterstock.com

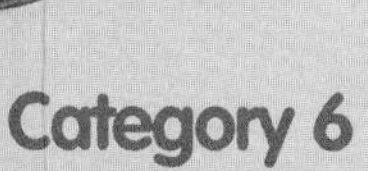

More **TORNADOES** form in the **UNITED STATES OF AMERICA** than any other **COUNTRY** on the **PLANET.**

CATEGORY
1

# ACTIVE EARTH

**1** **What is the Earth's core made of?**

a. Metal b. Rock c. Crystal

**2** **How many earthquakes does Japan have each year?**

a. Around 50 b. Around 500 c. Around 1,500

**3** **How old is the Earth?**

a. 4.5 million years old
b. 4.5 billion years old
c. 4.5 thousand years old

**4** **What is the world's tallest active volcano?**

a. Mt Fuji
b. Mt Etna
c. Mauna Loa

**5** **How thick is the Earth's crust?**

a. 8–80 km
b. 100–1,000 km
c. 50–500 km

**6** **What does 'tsunami' mean in Japanese?**

a. Ocean mountain
b. Great harbour wave
c. Giant sea

**7** **If you could drill a hole from the north to the south pole, how long would it take for you to fall from one side to the other, if you jumped in?**

a. About 40 minutes
b. About 4 hours
c. About 4 days

**8**

**What is the world's most powerful geyser?**

a. Old Faithful
b. Steamboat Geyser
c. Fly Geyser

**9**

**What is the name of the hot liquid rock found inside a volcano?**

a. Lava b. Magma
c. Molten

**10**

**What instrument is used to measure an earthquake?**

a. Geiger counter
b. Seismograph
c. Spectroscope

**11**

**What is the scale used to measure earthquakes called?**

a. Richter scale
b. Moment magnitude scale
c. Pascal scale

**12**

**What is the middle section of the Earth, between the crust and the core, called?**

a. Middle-earth
b. Mantle
c. Thanosphere

**13**

**What was the world's largest recorded volcanic eruption?**

a. Mount Tambora, 1815
b. Vesuvius, 79 CE
c. Krakatoa, 1883

**14**

**How fast can a tsunami travel?**

a. Up to 160 kph (100 mph)
b. Up to 480 kph (300 mph)
c. Up to 970 kph (600 mph)

**DID YOU KNOW?**

Volcanoes can be found on land and on the ocean floor.

# ACTIVE EARTH

**1**

**a. Metal.**

Both the inner and outer cores are made of super-hot iron and nickel.

**2**

**c. Around 1,500.**

Situated on the 'Pacific Ring of Fire', Japan experiences minor tremors every day.

**3**

**b. 4.5 billion years old.**

The planet formed as a rotating disc of rocks and gases that came together due to the force of gravity.

**4**

**c. Mauna Loa.**

Mauna Loa in Hawaii measures over 17 km from base to tip. Most of the volcano is below sea level.

**5**

**a. 8–80 km.**

Under the oceans, the crust is only 8 km thick, while it averages around 40 km thick under the land.

**6**

**b. Great harbour wave.**

Tsunamis can reach heights of 35 m (about the same height as a 10-storey building).

**7**

**a. About 40 minutes.**

If you could jump down a hole that went all the way through the Earth, you'd reach speeds up to 28,000 kmh.

# QUIZ 1 ANSWERS

**8**

**b. Steamboat Geyser.**

Steamboat Geyser in Yellowstone National Park (USA) can shoot water up to 120 m (400 ft) into the air!

**9**

**b. Magma.**

Material inside a volcano is called magma. When it comes out during an eruption, it is called lava.

**10**

**b. Seismograph.**

A seisomograph draws a line, that wiggles as the earth beneath it moves.

**11**

**b. Moment magnitude scale.**

The moment magnitude scale has replaced the Richter scale to measure the size of earthquakes across the planet.

**12**

**b. Mantle.**

The mid-section of the planet stretches 3,000 km beneath the crust. It's hot enough down there to melt rock (3,000°C).

**13**

**a. Mount Tambora, 1815.**

The eruption had more energy than 2 million atomic bombs.

**14**

**c. Up to 970 kph (600 mph).**

Sometimes, before a tsunami hits, there is a 'vaccuum effect' that sucks water from harbours and beaches.

# EXPLORE THE CONTINENTS

**1** **Africa has been moving towards Europe for millions of years. How fast is Africa moving?**
a. 2 metres per year b. 2.5 centimetres per year c. 30 centimetres per year

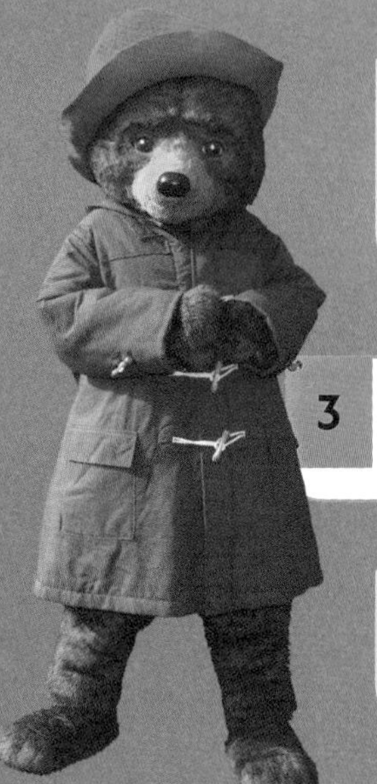

**2** **350 million years ago, all of today's continents were joined together in one massive supercontinent. What was it called?**
a. Pangea b. Unuma c. Miyagi

**3** **Paddington Bear is famously from Peru. On which continent would you find Peru?**
a. South America b. North America c. Asia

**4** **How many continents are there?**
a. Five b. Six c. Seven

**5** **Look at the picture to the right. Which continent is this?**
a. South America b. Africa c. Asia

**6** **What is the name of the canal that separates North America from South America?**
a. Panama Canal b. Colombia Canal c. The Americas Canal

**7** **Which continent has the highest and the lowest points of land on the planet?**
a. North America b. Asia c. South America

**8** **Which continent has the largest island?**
a. Africa b. North America c. Europe

**DID YOU KNOW?**

**Asia is the the largest continent in the world.**

**9** **What is the smallest continent?**
a. Antarctica b. Europe c. Oceania

**10** **Which continent has the longest railway?**
a. Asia b. South America c. Africa

**11** **Which of the continents has the most countries in it?**
a. Europe b. Africa c. Asia

**12** **The Himalayan mountain range was formed when the Indian subcontinent collided with this continent, pushing the land up into the tallest peaks on the planet.**
a. South America b. Asia c. Africa

**13** **Which is the driest continent?**
a. Asia b. Africa c. Antarctica

**14** **What is another name given to the continent of Oceania?**
a. Australia b. Gondwana c. Pacifica

# EXPLORE THE CONTINENTS

1 **b. 2.5 centimetres per year.** Africa is moving towards Europe at roughly the same rate as your fingernails grow.

2 **a. Pangea.** Some scientists predict that some of the continents will join back together. But it won't be for another 250 million years!

3 **a. South America.** This famous bear's full name is Paddington Brown, after the train station in London and the Brown family who found and adopted him there.

4 **c. Seven.** Although there are seven continents now, the plates of land on the crust of the planet are always moving: some are moving further apart while others are crashing together.

5 **b. Africa.** Africa is a massive continent, accounting for about 20% of all the land on Earth.

6 **a. Panama Canal.** The canal was opened in 1914 and has seen over a million ships pass through its locks.

7 **b. Asia.** Asia is home to the highest point on earth (Mount Everest) as well as the lowest point on land (The Dead Sea).

The level of salt in the Dead Sea make it easy to float in.

# QUIZ 2 ANSWERS

**8** **b. North America.** Although Greenland is a country within the Danish Kingdom, the island itself is on the North American continental plate.

**9** **c. Oceania.** Although it is the smallest, Oceania contains more than 10,000 islands in the Pacific, spread over thousands of miles.

**10** **a. Asia.** The Trans-Siberian Railway runs for over 9,289 km, travelling from Moscow in the west to Vladivostok in the east. It takes seven days to get from one end to the other.

**11** **b. Africa.** Around a quarter of the world's countries can be found in Africa.

**12** **b. Asia.** The continents are still colliding with each other, meaning that the Himalayas get slightly taller each year.

**13** **c. Antarctica.** It's the windiest, driest and coldest of the continents, with temperatures dropping to below -80°C.

**14** **a. Australia.** This content contains the country of Australia. The continent is called Oceania in recognition of the thousands of islands in the Pacific Ocean that it contains.

# WORLD FLAGS

**1**

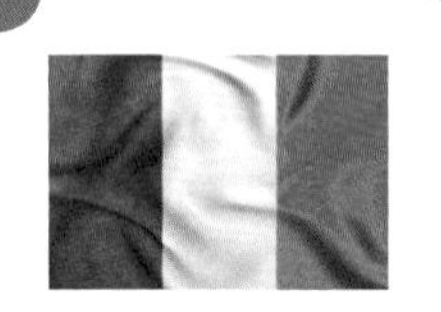

**This is the flag of which country?**

a. France
b. Italy
c. Spain

**2**

**Which country's flag has a red maple leaf at its centre?**

a. New Zealand
b. Thailand
c. Canada

**3**

**This is the flag of which country?**

a. Saudi Arabia
b. Pakistan
c. India

**4**

**The flag of Japan is made up of which two colours?**

a. Red and white
b. Red and yellow
c. Red and blue

**5**

**Which is the only national flag to feature a tree in its design?**

a. Lebanon
b. Ghana
c. Finland

**6**

**How many stars appear on the flag of the United States of America?**

a. 48
b. 50
c. 52

**7**

**Which constellation appears on the flag of New Zealand?**

a. Ursa Major
b. The Southern Cross
c. Orion

**8**

**What is unusual about the flag of Nepal?**

a. It changes every year
b. It has eight colours in it
c. It isn't rectangular

**DID YOU KNOW?**

**The United Kingdom flag is known as the 'Union Jack'.**

**9**

**This is the flag of which country?**

a. Ireland
b. India
c. Nigeria

**10**

**What name is given to the flag of Scotland?**

a. Saint Andrew's Cross
b. Saint Wallace's Cross
c. Saint Robert's Cross

**11**

**This is the flag of which country?**

a. Norway
b. Sweden
c. Greece

**12**

**Which two colours feature on the flags of Monaco and Poland?**

a. Red and yellow
b. Red and white
c. White and yellow

**13**

**What is the commonly used name for the skull and crossbones design of the pirate flag?**

a. Jolly Roger
b. Billy Bones
c. Merry Marauder

**14**

**Which country's flag has a yellow 5-pointed star against a red background?**

a. China
b. Vietnam
c. Chile

**DID YOU KNOW?**

**The colours of the Brazil flag represent the country's forests (green) and wealth from gold (yellow).**

# WORLD FLAGS

**1**

**a. France.**
The French flag is known as 'Le drapeau tricolore', which means 'the tricolour flag'.

**2**

**c. Canada.**
The maple leaf is recognised as a symbol of Canada.

**3**

**b. Pakistan.**
Pakistan is a mainly Muslim country. The star on the flag represents the five pillars of Islam.

**4**

**a. Red and white.**
The Japanese flag shows a red rising sun on a white field.

**5**

**a. Lebanon.**
The tree in the Lebanese flag is a cedar tree and symbolises the Christian religion.

**6**

**b. 50.**
Each star on the United States of America flag represents one of the country's 50 states.

**7**

**b. The Southern Cross.**
The Southern Cross also features on other countries' flags, including Australia and Papua New Guinea.

**8**

**c. It isn't rectangular.**
The crimson red in Nepal's flag represents bravery.

**DID YOU KNOW?**

**The USA flag has the nickname 'Star-spangled Banner' and 'Old Glory'.**

**9**

**b. India.**
The spoked circle at the centre of India's flag represents the 'wheel of law' or dharma, signifying the progress of the nation through change.

**10**

**a. Saint Andrew's Cross**
The cross is said to be the same shape as the cross Saint Andrew was crucified on.

**11**

**a. Norway.**
The Norwegian national flag uses a design of a Nordic cross, using the colours of neighbouring countries and those of 'freedom' (the red, white and blue of France, the United Kingdom and the United States of America).

**12**

**b. Red and white.**
The flags of Monaco and Poland are quite easy to get mixed up: Monaco has a red horizontal stripe at the top and a white stripe below. Poland's flag is the exact opposite, with a white stripe at the top and a red one beneath.

**13**

**a. Jolly Roger.**
Nobody knows for sure how the skull and crossbones design came to be known as the Jolly Roger, but it may be from the French 'Jolie Rouge' meaning 'Pretty Red'.

**14**

**b. Vietnam.**
Each point of the star on the flag of Vietnam represents the people of the country: workers, peasants, soldiers, intellectuals, and businessmen.

# IN THE **WATER**

**1**

**What is the world's largest ocean?**

a. Pacific Ocean
b. Atlantic Ocean
c. Indian Ocean

**2**

**How deep is the Mariana Trench, the deepest ocean trench in the world?**

a. 11 km b. 1 km
c. 22 km

**3**

**How much of the world's oxygen is produced by the oceans?**

a. 5% b. 40% c. 70%

**4**

**How much of global beach litter is made up of plastic?**

a. 3% b. 53% c. 73%

**5**

**What is the world's smallest ocean?**

a. Indian Ocean
b. Atlantic Ocean
c. Arctic Ocean

**6**

**The longest mountain range on Earth is under the ocean. But which one?**

a. Pacific Ocean
b. Atlantic Ocean
c. Indian Ocean

**7**

**How many different species of sea creatures have been found to have eaten or become entangled in plastic?**

a. 200
b. 700
c. 1,500

**8**

**What is a seamount?**

a. A type of whale
b. An underwater mountain
c. Another name for a dolphin

**9**

**What name is given to the flat part of the ocean floor?**

a. Abyssal plain
b. Gulf stream
c. Sea chasm

**10**

**How much of the Earth's oceans have been explored by humans?**

a. 5% b. 40% c. 60%

**11**

**Why is the sea salty?**

a. From salty rocks on the sea floor
b. From minerals being washed into the sea from the land
c. From 'salty rain'

**12**

**What greenhouse gas does the ocean absorb?**

a. Methane
b. Carbon dioxide
c. Neon

**13**

**The Great Pacific Garbage Patch, a collection of mostly plastic waste between Hawaii and California, is roughly:**

a. Half the size of France
b. The same size as France
c. Three times the size of France

**14**

**What sea has the highest salt content?**

a. The Mediterranean Sea
b. The Dead Sea
c. The Caspian Sea

# IN THE WATER

**1**

**a. Pacific.**

The Pacific Ocean is so huge it covers over 30% of the surface of the planet.

**2**

**a. 11 km.**

The trench is so deep that if you put Mount Everest in it, the top of the mountain would still be 2 km underwater!

**3**

**c. 70%.**

The ocean produces oxygen through the plants and tiny plant-like animals that live in it.

**4**

**c. 73%.**

Unless we do something about it, it is predicted that, by 2050, virtually every seabird species on the planet will be eating plastic.

**5**

**c. Arctic Ocean.**

Although it is the smallest of the four main oceans, it still spans over 15 million square kilometres.

**6**

**b. Atlantic Ocean.**

The mid-ocean ridge is an underwater mountain range that runs for 65,000 km along the floor of the Atlantic ocean.

**7**

**b. 700.**

It has been estimated that more than 5 trillion pieces of plastic waste are floating in the world's oceans.

## QUIZ 4 ANSWERS

**8**

**b. An underwater mountain.**

These are usually formed from extinct underwater volcanoes.

**9**

**a. Abyssal plain.**

Scientists have very little data on the deepest depths of the ocean, which means it is a great area to explore.

**10**

**a. 5%.**

We know more about the surface of the moon than we do about our own oceans. Time to get exploring!

**11**

**b. From minerals being washed into the sea from the land.**

It also comes from minerals blasted out of geothermal vents on the sea floor.

**12**

**b. Carbon dioxide.**

The oceans absorb about 30% of the carbon dioxide released into the atmosphere. However, this makes the ocean more acidic.

**13**

**c. Three times the size of France.**

The garbage patch has tangles of abandoned fishing nets, known as 'ghost nets.'

**14**

**b. The Dead Sea**

The Dead Sea is so salty, you can't sink in it! The Dead Sea is nearly 33% salt. Normal seawater only has about 3% salt in it.

# WHAT'S THE WEATHER?

**1**

**What is the centre of a hurricane called?**

a. The eye
b. The mouth
c. The fulcrum

**2**

**What is the scientific name for a thunderstorm cloud?**

a. Stratocumulus
b. Cumulonimbus
c. Altonimbus

**3**

**When a puddle dries up in the sun, it has...**

a. Evaporated
b. Transpirated
c. Respirated

**4**

**How often does lightning strike the surface of the Earth?**

a. 1 time per second
b. 10 times per second
c. 100 times per second

**5**

**What does a barometer measure?**

a. Temperature
b. Atmospheric pressure
c. Wind speed

**6**

**What is the scale used for measuring the strength of tornadoes?**

a. Fujita
b. Twister
c. Tatsumaki

**7**

**Which city has the most sunshine per year?**

a. Yuma, United States
b. Doha, Qatar
c. Athens, Greece

# QUIZ 5

## 8

**What is the name of the super-fast air currents high up in the atmosphere?**

a. Jet stream
b. Gulf jet
c. Wind tunnel

## 9

**What effect can exposure to sunlight have on your hair?**

a. Make it grow faster
b. Change its colour
c. Make it curlier

## 10

**Weather patterns, when observed over a long period of time, are called:**

a. Climate
b. Forecast
c. Predictions

## 11

**What is hail?**

a. Snow flurries
b. Balls of ice
c. Strong wind

## 12

**What aspect of the weather most threatens coral reefs?**

a. A warming climate
b. Hailstorms
c. Whirlpools

## 13

**What is one positive aspect of forest fires?**

a. They kill dangerous pests
b. They enrich the soil
c. They can create glass

## 14

**Sirocco, Chinook and Mistral are all types of what?**

a. Wind
b. Beach
c. Weather instrument

# WHAT'S THE WEATHER?

## 1

**a. The Eye.**

In the centre of the hurricane, the 'eye', the clouds disappear and the wind drops. However, this circle of calm is surrounded by the eye-wall, where the strongest, most violent parts of the storm are.

## 2

**b. Cumulonimbus.**

'Cumulo' means heaped up in Latin. 'Nimbus' means rainstorm. Thunderstorm clouds can grow to be over 10 km tall!

## 3

**a. Evaporated.**

Water molecules at the surface of the puddle are jiggled about by the energy of the sun and the wind and so get detached from the liquid puddle, turning into water vapour. Gradually, the whole puddle is 'vapourised' in evaporation.

## 4

**c. 100 times per second.**

Lightning is a sudden bright electrical discharge of energy that can be 5 times hotter than the surface of the sun! The thunderclap that accompanies it is the sound of the shockwave made by the lightning.

## 5

**b. Atmospheric pressure.**

Atmospheric pressure is a measure of the weight of the air in the atmosphere, which varies with the weather: warmer air is less dense than colder air. This is what a barometer detects.

## 6

**a. Fujita.**

No-one knows exactly how tornadoes form, but these twisting columns of air can reach speeds of 480 km (300 miles) per hour.

# QUIZ 5 ANSWERS

## 7

**a. Yuma, United States**

The Yuma desert, a region of the Sonora desert in the southwest of the United States receives over 90% sunshine, which is over 4,000 hours per year!

## 8

**a. Jet stream.**

These high roads of wind help to drive the global weather system and reach speeds of 440 km (275 miles) per hour.

## 9

**b. Change its colour.**

Hair is coloured by melanin, a pigment that also gives a person's skin and eyes their colour. Sunlight can damage the melanin in hair, making it lighter.

## 10

**a. Climate.**

Climate describes patterns of weather over years. Scientists all agree that climate change – global warming – is happening.

## 11

**b. Balls of ice.**

Hailstones can be round or they can be jagged. They are between 0.5 and 20 cm in diameter.

## 12

**a. A warming climate.**

Coral reefs across the world, including the Great Barrier Reef that runs off the east coast of Australia, are becoming bleached and dead due to warming ocean temperatures as a result of climate change.

## 13

**b. They enrich the soil.**

Although they can be devastating for both human and other animal populations, forest fires are also part of a natural cycle in which the ashes of the burnt trees and plants feed the soil to help the next generation of trees grow.

## 14

**a. Wind.**

The Chinook wind blows across the praries of Canada. The Sirocco wind starts in the Sahara desert and blows north towards Italy.

# NAME THAT COUNTRY

**1** **Which country has the most lakes?**
a. Canada b. Russia c. China

**2** **Which two countries are home to the tallest mountain in the world?**
a. India and Pakistan b. China and Nepal c. Argentina and Chile

**3** **Belgium is famous for producing which confectionary?**
a. Toffee b. Chocolate c. Eclairs

**4** **The Great Pyramids are found in which country?**
a. Libya b. Egypt c. Sudan

**5** **The country of Ghana is on which continent?**
a. Africa b. South America c. Asia

**6** **Which country is famous for pasta and pizza?**
a. Greece b. India c. Italy

**7** **What is the smallest country in the world?**
a. Liechtenstein b. St Lucia c. Vatican City

**8** **Which country is home to most of the Amazon Rainforest?**
a. Sudan b. Argentina c. Brazil

**9** **In which country might you climb up Table Mountain?**
a. South Africa b. Brazil c. Russia

**10** **Which country is named after both the trinity and the tobacco crop?**
a. Trinidad and Tobago b. Papua New Guinea c. St Kitts and Nevis

**11** **In which of these countries might you see the Northern Lights?**
a. Spain b. Indonesia c. Norway

**12** **Look at the picture to the left. Which European country is this?**
a. Germany b. France c. Denmark

**13** **Suomi is the local name for which European country?**
a. Norway b. Sweden c. Finland

**14** **In which country would you find the city of Dubai?**
a. New Zealand b. UAE c. Yemen

**DID YOU KNOW?**

**South Sudan is the world's newest country.**

# NAME THAT COUNTRY

**1** **a. Canada.** Some estimates go higher then 2 million lakes.

**2** **b. China and Nepal.** Called 'Sagamartha' in Nepali or 'Chomolungma' in Tibetan, the tallest peak in the world reaches over 8 km above sea level.

**3** **b. Chocolate.** Belgium is one of the world's biggest exporters of chocolate, exporting hundreds of thousands of tonnes of it per year.

**4** **b. Egypt.** The pyramids at Giza were the tallest structures on Earth for nearly 4,000 years.

**5** **a. Africa.** Lake Volta in the West African country of Ghana is the largest artificial reservoir in the world by surface area, covering over 8, 500 square kilometres!

**6** **c. Italy.** Italy is a boot-shaped peninsula that juts out into the sea in the south of Europe. Northern Italy is home to part of the Alps mountain range, while in the south there are hot farmlands that grow olives, almonds and other crops.

**7** **c. Vatican City.** This state is so small it sits inside another city, Rome, which is the capital city of Italy. It is home to the Pope, the leader of the Roman Catholic church.

# QUIZ 6 ANSWERS

**8** **c. Brazil.** Brazil is the largest country in the South American continent. The Amazon rainforest gets its name from the mighty Amazon river that flows through the north of the country.

**9** **a. South Africa.** Table Mountain gets its name from its long flat top, called a plateau. The mountain overlooks the city of Cape Town in the south of the country.

**10** **a. Trinidad and Tobago.** These islands, the most southerly in the Caribbean, have lush rainforests and are home to the islands' national bird – the scarlet ibis.

**11** **c. Norway.** The amazing natural light-show of the Northern Lights, or Aurora Borealis, can be seen in countries in the Arctic Circle, such as Norway.

**12** **b. France.** France is western Europe's largest country. It has borders with Belgium, Germany, Spain, Italy and Switzerland.

**13** **c. Finland.** Finland is in the northeast of Europe, between Sweden, Norway and Russia. Lapland, in the north of Finland, has a Santa Claus village that is open all year round.

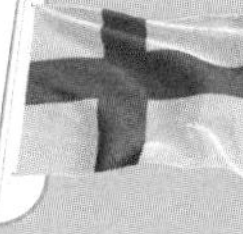

**DID YOU KNOW?**

**Russia is the world's largest country.**

**14** **b. UAE.** Dubai is a modern city with cutting-edge architecture. It is home to the world's tallest structure –The Burj Khalifa.

# WORLD LANDSCAPES

**1**

**What is a hill made entirely out of sand called?**

a. A dune b. A bunker
c. A mound

**2**

**What mountainous feature might be called a river of ice?**

a. An avalanche
b. A glacier
c. An iceberg

**3**

**The place where a river meets the sea is called...**

a. An outlet
b. An estuary
c. A seajoin

**4**

**The Great Plains of North America are called this because...**

a. They have lots of airports
b. They are flat
c. They have the most rivers

**5**

**Which country does the word 'landscape' originate from?**

a. The Netherlands
b. Germany
c. Slovakia

**6**

**What type of landscape is a canyon?**

a. A coastal bay
b. A hole in the ground
c. A collection of small hills

**7** **If you described a landscape as being a plateau, it would look...**

a. Spiky b. Flat c. Lumpy

**8** **What type of harsh, treeless landscape is found at the tops of mountains and in the Arctic?**

a. Tundra b. Tropical c. Temperate

**9** **Approximately how many people live in desert areas?**

a. 1 million b. 5 million
c. 1 billion

**10** **Where might you see features such as stalactites and stalagmites?**

a. Caves b. Beaches
c. Rainforests

**11** **Sometimes, valleys can be so huge they stretch across countries. What are these called?**

a. Scars b. Rifts
c. Gorges

**12** **Where are the largest crystal caves in the world?**

a. Thailand b. Mexico
c. France

**13** **What is the only continent on Earth that doesn't have rainforests?**

a. Europe b. Antarctica
c. North America

**14** **What is the name of the long mountain range that runs down the side of South America?**

a. The Handies b. The Andes
c. The Whaties

# WORLD LANDSCAPES

**1**

**a. A dune.**

In some desert areas, sand dunes created by swirling winds fill the landscape from horizon to horizon.

**2**

**b. A glacier.**

You can think of glaciers as being giant rivers made out of ice. They are immensely heavy, slow and powerful so as they move, they carve out great valleys between mountains.

**3**

**b. An estuary.**

An estuary is a wide, flat part of a river where freshwater meets seawater. It can also be called a lagoon, a bay, a slough or a sound.

**4**

**b. They are flat.**

The Great Plains of North America are grasslands. They have been home to peoples for tens of thousands of years.

**5**

**a. The Netherlands**

'Landscape' comes from the Dutch word 'landschap', which means a painting of the countryside.

**6**

**b. A hole in the ground.**

The Grand Canyon in Arizona, USA is 446 km (277 miles) long. It took the Colorado river 5–6 million years to carve out this natural wonder.

# QUIZ 7 ANSWERS

**7**

**b. Flat.**

A plateau is like a hill with the pointy bit sliced off, leaving a large flat top.

**8**

**a. Tundra.**

Although these are some of the harshest environments on Earth, plants and animals (such as Arctic foxes and polar bears) live in the Arctic tundra.

**9**

**c. 1 billion.**

Deserts cover around 20% of the planet's land. Desertification – a process where areas become deserts – is increasing as humans cut down forests and move into the area.

**10**

**a. Caves.**

A stalagtite looks like an icicle made out of rock. It is formed by tiny bits of rock building up as water drips from the roof of a cave.

**11**

**b. Rifts.**

The 'Great Rift Valley' is actually a series of connected valleys that stretches from Jordan in the Middle East all the way to southern Africa.

**12**

**b. Mexico.**

The Crystal Cave in Mexico has giant crystals of the mineral gypsum. These crystals are 11 m (36 feet) long and weigh 55 tonnes.

**13**

**b. Antarctica.**

Rainforests need a lot of energy from the sun. Antarctica is not only extremely cold, it is also dark for nearly half of the year.

**14**

**b. The Andes.**

This mountain range is over 7,000 km (4,300 miles) long and is home to the tallest mountain not in Asia. This is Mount Aconcagua in Argentina.

# CAPITAL CITIES

**1** **Which capital city, that sounds like the name of its country, was designed in the mid-20th century?**
a. Mexico City b. Brasilia c. San Salvador

**2** **On what continent is Oagadougou, capital of Burkina Faso?**
a. Africa b. Asia c. Australia

**3** **Which world capital is located on the River Thames?**
a. Paris b. London c. Washington D.C.

**4** **What is the capital city of Spain?**
a. Rome b. Madrid c. Vienna

**5** **Seoul is the capital city of which country?**
a. South Korea b. Japan c. Malaysia

**6** **Which capital city is home to the Kremlin and Red Square?**
a. Cairo b. Baghdad c. Moscow

**7** **Which of these 'Ports' is the capital city of Papua New Guinea?**
a. Port Lessive b. Port Moresby c. Port Sames

# QUIZ 8

**8** **Tokyo is the capital city of which country?**
a. Japan b. China c. Vietnam

**9** **Complete this saying with the name of a capital city: All roads lead to....**
a. Paris b. Rome c. Bangkok

**10** **The Eiffel Tower is a world-famous landmark in which capital city?**
a. Bernew b. Dublin c. Paris

**11** **This Danish capital city was home to the children's author Hans Christian Andersen.**
a. Copenhagen b. Oslo c. Stockholm

South Africa has three capital cities: Cape Town, Pretoria and Bloemfontein.

**12** **This boot-like name is the capital of New Zealand.**
a. Moccasin b. Wellington c. Sandaltown

**13** **Which capital city can be found next to the Great Pyramids?**
a. Algiers b. Tunis c. Cairo

**14** **Which of these capital cities is criss-crossed with canals and is synonymous with cyclists ?**
a. Brussels b. Amsterdam c. Athens

# CAPITAL CITIES

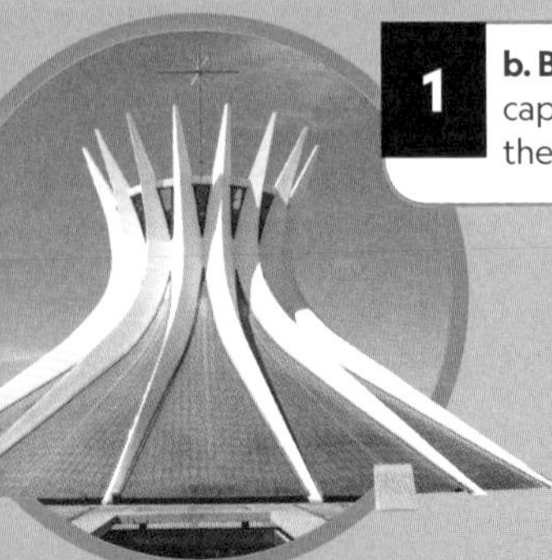

**1** **b. Brasilia.** It was decided to move the capital city of Brazil from Rio, which is on the coast, to a more central location.

**a. Africa.** The country's name – Burkina Faso – means 'land of the incorruptible people'.

**3** **b. London.** An icon of the capital city of England, Big Ben and the Houses of Parliament sit on the banks of the River Thames.

**b. Madrid.** A historic city in the centre of Spain, Madrid is home to the Museo del Prado, a museum over 200 years old.

**a. South Korea.** Seoul is a megacity, home to over 10 million people, where towering skyscrapers sit alongside ancient Buddhist temples.

**6** **c. Moscow.** At one end of Moscow's Red Square sits the famous St Basil's Cathedral with its swirling multicoloured domes with golden spires.

**b. Port Moresby.** Papua New Guinea is home to the most languages in the world. Over 800 languages are spoken across the country.

# QUIZ 8 ANSWERS

**8** **a. Japan.** Tokyo hosts many impressive annual festivals, including a display with over 20,000 fireworks, and a festival involving 10,000 traditional Japanese dancers.

**9** **b. Rome.** Rome is an ancient city. The Pantheon is a temple, with the largest unreinforced concrete dome in the world.

**10** **c. Paris.** Gustave Eiffel, who designed the famous tower also helped build the Statue of Liberty in New York, USA.

**11** **a. Copenhagen.** Hans Christian Andersen is famous for writing such classic stories as The Little Mermaid and The Emperor's New Clothes.

**12** **b. Wellington.** Wellington has a historic cable car, built in the 1800s that goes from the centre of the city to the nearby hills and beautiful botanical gardens.

**13** **c. Cairo.** Cairo, the capital city of Egypt, lies on the longest river in the world: the river Nile.

**14** **b. Amsterdam.** The Anne Frank museum in Amsterdam is built around the house where Anne Frank and her family hid during the Second World War. The museum attracts 1.2 million visitors per year.

# GLOBAL TRADITIONS

## 1

**Europe's biggest annual street party is in which city?**

a. London
b. Rome
c. Paris

## 2

**The biggest carnival in the world is in which South American country?**

a. Brazil
b. Peru
c. Argentina

## 3

**The bar mitzvah is a tradition in which religion?**

a. Judaism
b. Christianity
c. Hinduism

## 4

**What is the name for the Hindu Festival of Colour?**

a. Holi
b. Raga
c. Peela

## 5

**Which tradition would you associate trick-or-treating with?**

a. Christmas
b. Halloween
c. Easter

## 6

**What is the name of the 'evil' version of Santa Claus in this tradition from Germany and Austria?**

a. Krampus
b. Moloch
c. Elfeater

## 7

**Where is the world's largest food fight held?**

a. Italy
b. France
c. Spain

### 8

**What is the Haka?**

a. A war dance
b. A food festival
c. A holiday

### 9

**What food is traditionally eaten in the United States during Thanksgiving?**

a. Pork
b. Turkey
c. Lamb

### 10

**Which country celebrates Burns Night?**

a. Scotland
b. Ireland
c. Wales

### 11

**Bonfire night in the UK celebrates what?**

a. An attempt to murder a king
b. An attempt to blow up the Houses of Parliament
c. An attempt to drain the River Thames.

### 12

**How is the Dalai Lama, the Buddhist leader, selected?**

a. By selecting certain objects
b. By walking a tightrope blindfolded
c. By holding their breath underwater for a minute

### 13

**Independence Day in the United States falls on which date?**

a. 4th July
b. 5th August
c. 3rd June

### 14

**What foodstuff is rolled down a hill in this odd tradition from the UK?**

a. Bread
b. Cheese
c. Apples

# GLOBAL TRADITIONS

## 1

**a. London.**

The Notting Hill Carnival is a massive street party that takes place in August and celebrates Caribbean culture.

## 2

**a. Brazil.**

The highlight of the Carnival in Rio de Janeiro is the Samba Parades, where schools of between 3,000 and 5,000 samba dancers (from each school!) battle it out.

## 3

**a. Judaism.**

A bar mitzvah is a Jewish celebration of the coming-of-age for boys. For girls, it is called a bat mitzvah.

## 4

**a. Holi.**

This Hindu festival is famous for people throwing colourful pigments over each other. Each pigment means something: red symbolises love and marriage, blue represents the god Krishna, and green symbolises new beginnings.

## 5

**b. Halloween.**

All Hallow's Eve, now celebrated as Halloween across the world, used to be called Samhain and was a tradition that had been observed for thousands of years.

## 6

**a. Krampus.**

'Krampus night' is celebrated on 5 December in Austria. While Santa (St Nicholas) gives good children presents, Krampus is supposed to beat children with sticks, put them in his sack and take them away.

## 7

**c. Spain.**

'La Tomatina' is a massive food fight in a tiny town called Buñol in Spain. Because of its popularity, the authorities have limited the number of people allowed to take part to 20,000.

## 8

**a. A war dance.**
The Maori people of New Zealand used the Haka as a war dance, designed to strike fear into their opponents. It is now more commonly seen when the New Zealand rugby team, the All Blacks, play their games.

## 9

**b. Turkey.**
The US national holiday of Thanksgiving was established by President Abraham Lincoln in 1863, to promote unity across the country.

## 10

**a. Scotland.**
Burns Night celebrates the life of the Scottish poet, Robert Burns. People typically eat a traditional meal of haggis, neeps (turnips) and tatties (potatoes).

## 11

**b. An attempt to blow up the Houses of Parliament.**
The bonfires of 5 November actually celebrate the burning alive of Guy Fawkes, who was one of the people who had plotted to blow up the Houses of Parliament in 1605.

## 12

**a. By selecting certain objects.**
The high lamas of the Buddhist faith find a candidate and ask them to select an object from a range of different things. If the candidate selects the object that once belonged to the previous Dalai Lama, it is taken as a sign that they should be the new one.

## 13

**a. 4th July.**
The declaration of independence was approved on 4 July and was signed on 2 August 1776.

## 14

**b. Cheese.**
The cheese in question is Double Gloucester, which participants send down a hill at speeds of up to 70 miles per hour!

# All things HISTORY

CATEGORY 2

In ANCIENT EGYPT, BODIES of the DEAD were placed in STONE containers called a SARCOPHAGUS.

# ANCIENT EGYPT

**1**

**What river provided the water that fuelled the civilisation in Ancient Egypt?**

a. The Nile
b. The Ganges
c. The Amazon

**2**

**The Pharaoh was the leader of the Ancient Egyptians. What does 'Pharaoh' translate as?**

a. Big king
b. Great house
c. Sun god

**3**

**How many gods and godesses did the Ancient Egyptians have?**

a. 200
b. 2,000
c. 20,000

**4**

**What is the name of the stone that enabled modern scientists to translate Ancient Egyptian hieroglyphics?**

a. Daisy Stone
b. Rosetta Stone
c. Tulippa Stone

**5**

**What is the name of the Ancient Egyptians' form of paper?**

a. Tablet
b. Papyrus
c. Leather

**6**

**What is an amulet?**

a. A type of good luck charm
b. A small mule
c. A brick used in building the pyramids

**7**

**How long did it take to build the Great Pyramid at Giza?**

a. 5 years
b. 10 years
c. 20 years

**8**

**What did canopic jars, found in the tombs of Pharaohs, hold?**

a. Gold coins
b. Body organs
c. Spices

# QUIZ 10

**9**

**How long would the bandages on a mummy be if you unrolled them all?**

a. 400 m
b. 1.6 km
c. 4 km

**10**

**Which Pharaoh's tomb was discovered by archaeologist Howard Carter?**

a. Tutankhamun
b. Cheops
c. Horus

**11**

**What was the name that the Ancient Egyptians gave to the Sun God?**

a. Ab
b. Ra
c. Thoth

**12**

**What was the Ancient Egyptians' favourite pet?**

a. Cat
b. Dog
c. Snake

**13**

**Hapi, an Egyptian god with a pot belly and blue skin, was the god of what?**

a. Illness
b. The underworld
c. The Nile

**14**

**What was the name of a board game played by the Ancient Egyptians?**

a. Shabti
b. Senet
c. Sobek

**15**

**What does 'The Sphinx' mean in Arabic?**

a. The Riddle of the Desert
b. The Father of Terror
c. The Lion Man

# ANCIENT EGYPT

**1**

**a. The Nile.**
The annual flooding of the Nile provided the surrounding land with nutrients, which encouraged people to settle there.

**2**

**b. Great house.**
While early Egyptian rulers were called 'King', the name Pharaoh, which referred to the home of the king, became the name of the rulers.

**3**

**b. 2,000.**
The Ancient Egyptians had gods and godesses for almost everything you could think of.

**4**

**b. Rosetta Stone.**
The stone has the same text written in three different languages. One of these was hieroglyphics, which helped people decode the ancient writing.

**5**

**b. Papyrus.**
The Egyptians cut or peeled the stalks of papyrus reeds into long strips, laid them in two layers, one vertical and one horizontal, then pressed and dried them to form a sheet.

**6**

**a. A type of good luck charm.**
Amulets were used to ward off sickness and were even given by doctors as treatments.

**7**

**c. 20 years.**
Built by a workforce of over 20,000, the Great Pyramid was made for a Pharaoh named Khufu.

**8**

**b. Body organs.**
These jars were used during the process of mummification and stored the stomach, lungs, liver and intestines.

9

**b. 1.6 km.**
Mummification was the method of preserving the bodies of the dead.

10

**a. Tutankhamun.**
The tomb contained over 5,000 artifacts such as jewellery, chariots and clothes.

11

**b. Ra.**
It was believed that the Pharaohs were the offspring of the Sun God. Ra was said to travel through the sky on a boat.

12

**a. Cat.**
A cat was considered by the Ancient Egyptians to be a kind of good luck charm. Plus, cats keep mice and rats away!

13

**c. The Nile.**
This god was very important to the people of Egypt as he was responsible for the flooding of the Nile river, which gave life to the land.

14

**b. Senet.**
Senet was a game played by throwing sticks instead of dice. The people of Egypt played this game for over 2,000 years!

15

**b. The Father of Terror.**
The Sphinx is an ancient sculpture, over 4,500 years old. It shows a creature with the body of a lion and the head of a human.

# GREEKS AND ROMANS

**1** **What was the name of the Greek God of the sea?**
a. Athena b. Dionysus c. Poseidon

**2** **What was the name of the first king of Rome?**
a. Romulus b. Borgulus c. Vulcan

**3** **According to legend, Romulus and his brother Remus were raised by what type of animal?**
a. Octopus b. Wolf c. Tiger

**4** **How many spectators could fit in Rome's Colosseum?**
a. 10,000 b. 20,000 c. 50,000

**5** **Complete this well-known phrase: Rome wasn't built in a...**
a. Day b. Year c. Hurry

**6** **Who was Rome's first Emperor?**
a. Octavian b. Caesar c. Nero

**7** **The Roman invention, the aqueduct, was invented to transport what?**
a. Horses b. Water c. Corn

**8** **What was the official language of the Roman Empire?**
a. Latin b. Italian c. French

**9** **The Romans were impressive road builders. How many kilometres of road did the Empire build?**
a. 10,000 km b. 40,000 km c. 80,000 km

**DID YOU KNOW?**
Roman soldiers could march up to 40 km per day.

**10** **Which of these was a type of Roman soldier?**
a. Million b. Centurion
c. Trillion

**11** **Greek mythology is full of strange creatures. What was Medusa?**
a. A dog with three heads b. A woman with snakes for hair
c. A man with one eye

**12** **Which of these sporting events was created by the Ancient Greeks?**
a. The Olympics b. The World Cup c. The Champions League

**13** **Greece successfully invaded the city of Troy by playing a clever trick. What was it?**
a. They dug tunnels b. They hid in a wooden horse
c. They dressed up like a troupe of entertainers

**14** **Which of these forms of entertainment did the Ancient Greeks invent?**
a. Chess b. Theatre c. Volleyball

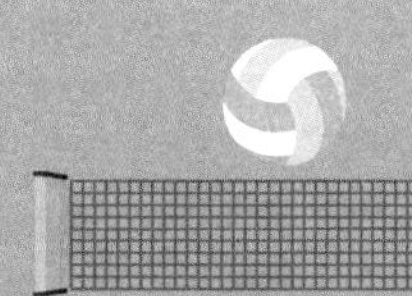

**15** **Which mountain in Greece did the Ancient Greeks think was the home of the gods?**
a. Mount Arrarat b. Mount Parnassus
c. Mount Olympus

# GREEKS AND ROMANS

**1** **c. Poseidon.** Poseidon wasn't the only god of the waters. In Ancient Greece there were others, such as Pontus, Nereus and Triton (who was Poseidon's son).

**2** **a. Romulus.** The city of Rome, from which the Roman Empire grew, was founded in 753 BC.

**3** **b. Wolf.** Also, according to legend, Romulus killed his brother to become the first ruler of Rome.

**4** **c. 50,000.** The massive structure was an arena where people would go to watch sporting events, games and gladiators in combat.

**5** **a. Day.** The phrase means that important work takes time and cannot be rushed.

**6** **a. Octavian.** Julius Caesar was Octavian's great uncle. After Julius Caesar's death, Octavian, whose family name was Augustus Caesar, became Emperor.

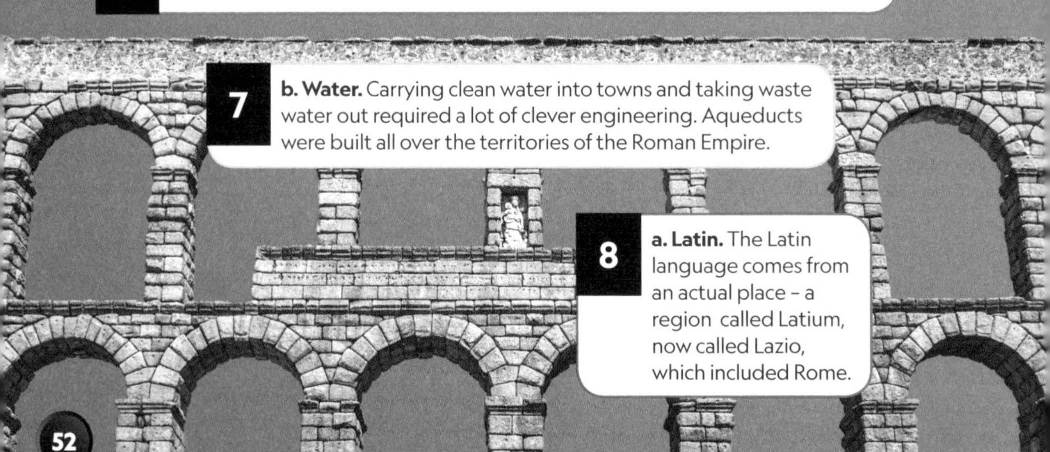

**7** **b. Water.** Carrying clean water into towns and taking waste water out required a lot of clever engineering. Aqueducts were built all over the territories of the Roman Empire.

**8** **a. Latin.** The Latin language comes from an actual place – a region called Latium, now called Lazio, which included Rome.

# QUIZ 11 ANSWERS

**9** **c. 80,000 km.** Roman roads stretched from England in the north, through Europe, and into Africa.

**10** **b. Centurion.** A centurion was a commanding officer in the Roman army. The centurion was in charge of a 'century', which meant a group of 100 soldiers.

**11** **b. A woman with snakes for her hair.** Medusa – a gorgon who could turn people into stone if they looked at her – was eventially defeated in the story by the hero, Perseus.

**12** **a. The Olympics.** Events in the Olympics of Ancient Greece included boxing, wrestling, long jump and chariot racing. But there was a twist: all competitors had to be naked!

**13** **b. They hid in a wooden horse.** The term 'Trojan horse' has come to mean anything that looks good on the outside, but has danger lurking within!

**14** **b. Theatre.** Most cities in Ancient Greece had a theatre. Some could hold audiences of 15,000 people!

**15** **c. Mount Olympus.** Standing at 2,197 m, the highest mountain in Greece, Mount Olympus was said to be the site of the throne of Zeus, the god who was the ruler of all the gods (and humans).

# ROYAL FAMILIES

Tsar Nicholas II

**1** What was the name of the king or queen of Russia?

a. Tsar or Tsarina
b. Pravda or Pravdina
c. Lider or Liderina

**2** Maharaja (for males) and Maharina (for females) were the names given to kings and queens in which country?

a. China b. India c. Japan

**3** How many wives did Henry VIII of England have?

a. 2 b. 4 c. 6

**4** The formal title of King Mswati III of the African Kingdom of eSwatini is 'Ngwenyama'. What does this word mean?

a. Lion b. Tiger c. Elephant

Queen Elizabeth I

**5** Queen Elizabeth I, who ruled during the time of Shakespeare, was the daughter of which English king?

a. George III
b. Henry VIII
c. Richard III

**6** What was the name of the mystic healer and adviser to the Russian royal family in the early 20th century?

a. Matzin
b. Rasputin
c. Opasnostin

Julius Caesar

**7** Julius Caesar, ruler of Rome, fell in love with which Egyptian queen?

a. Cleopatra
b. Nefertiti
c. Berenice

**8** The Mughal Emperor, Shah Jahan, built which world-famous landmark in the 1600s?

a. Guruvaya
b. Taj Mahal
c. Angkor Wat

**9** Which country has the oldest surviving royal family in Europe?

a. Denmark
b. England
c. Spain

**10** How long has the Japanese royal family reigned over the country?

a. 800 years
b. 1,400 years
c. 2,600 years

Emperor Akihito

# ROYAL FAMILIES

**1** **a. Tsar or Tsarina.**

Russia was ruled by one Royal family – the Romanovs – for over 300 years.

King Henry VIII

**2** **b. India.**

The great kings and queens of India and Pakistan ruled over different states. There were around 600 different states in India, each with their own king or queen.

**3** **c. 6.**

Henry VIII was a Tudor king of England in the 1500s.

**4** **a. Lion.**

The Kingdom of eSwatini, in Africa, used to be called Swaziland until the king decided to change it in 2018.

**5** **b. Henry VIII.**

Elizabeth was the daughter of Henry and his second wife, Anne Boelyn. Elizabeth's older half-sister, Mary, was queen before her.

**6** **b. Rasputin.**

Grigori Rasputin was hired by the Tsarina of Russia to try and heal her son, who suffered from a blood disease called haemophilia.

**7** **a. Cleopatra.**

Legend tells that Cleopatra hid in a rolled up carpet to be able to get close enough to Caesar to talk to him. They ended up falling in love.

**8** **b. Taj Mahal.**

The Emperor's third wife, Mumtaz Mahal, died during childbirth. Shah Jahan had the Taj Mahal built as a symbol of his love for her.

**9** **a. Denmark.**

Denmark has the longest unbroken line of rulers in Europe. Queen Margrethe II can trace her family back over 1,000 years.

**10** **c. 2,600 years.**

These days, the Japanese royal family has a symbolic role, but holds no real power.

Queen Margrethe II

# VIKINGS

TRUE or FALSE

1

MONDAY
TUESDAY
WEDNESDAY
THURSDAY
FRIDAY
SATURDAY
SUNDAY

We get our names for the days of the week from Vikings.

2

Viking helmets had horns stuck to either side.

3

Viking raiders weren't all male warriors.

4

Vikings are famous for their raids on the British Isles, but they also travelled as far as Canada and the Middle East.

5

Vikings were proud to call themselves 'Vikings'.

**6**

Many vikings came from South America.

**7**

The word 'Viking' means 'raider'.

**8**

The Vikings, not Christopher Columbus, were the first to 'discover' America.

**9**

Vikings called America 'The Land of Wine'.

**10**

Vikings carved dragons or sea-serpents onto the fronts of their boats, to scare people.

**DID YOU KNOW?**

Some Viking houses had grass roofs.

# VIKINGS

TRUE or FALSE

**1**

TRUE.
The names of Norse gods, worshipped by Viking people, are the basis for the names of the days of the week. Thursday, for example, refers to Thor, God of Thunder.

**2**

FALSE.
The famous horned helmet associated with Vikings was actually invented as a costume in the 1800s for use in plays and operas.

**3**

TRUE.
Women and children also joined in with the Vikings' military invasions.

**4**

TRUE.
Vikings were amazingly good sailors, navigators and explorers.

**5**

FALSE.
Vikings never referred to themselves by the name that we know them by.

## DID YOU KNOW?

The word 'berserk' comes from scary Viking warriors called 'Berserkers' who wore animal skins and howled like wild animals during battle.

## 6

**FALSE.**
Vikings came from an area of Europe called Scandanavia. Scandanavia is made up of Sweden, Norway and Denmark.

## 7

**TRUE.**
The word 'Viking' was more like a job title than a clue to where a person was from. There was no Viking-land. The Vikings came from all over Scandanavia in the north of Europe.

## 8

**TRUE.**
Of course, people had already been living on the North American continent for thousands of years before the Vikings turned up. But there is evidence that Leif Erikson, a Viking explorer, landed in Canada in around 1000 AD, beating Columbus by around 500 years.

## 9

**TRUE.**
When Leif Erikson landed in America, he was so impressed with the natural beauty and resources, that he named it 'Vinland', which means Land of Wine.

## 10

**TRUE.**
The Vikings' longboats had beautifully carved figureheads at the fronts. These depicted fearsome creatures to fill their enemies with dread.

# THE WORLD AT WAR

## 1

**How many World Wars have there been?**

a. 1
b. 2
c. 3

## 2

**The War of the Roses was about what?**

a. Controlling England
b. Controlling the trade of roses
c. Defeating the plague

## 3

**Which war ended at 11 minutes past 11 in the morning on the 11th day of the 11th month?**

a. World War I
b. World War II
c. Boer War

## 4

**Ares, the Greek god of war and destruction, had a throne made partially of...**

a. Swords
b. Human skin
c. Bones

## 5

**What type of animal was used to carry messages during World War I?**

a. Goats
b. Pigeons
c. Cats

## 6

**The war between the USA (and its allies) and Iraq in the 1990s was known as 'Desert what'?**

a. Storm
b. Offensive
c. Devils

## 7

**The woolly headgear, the balaclava, was named after a battle in which 19th century war?**

a. The Crimean War
b. The Napoleonic Wars
c. The War of the Gun

# QUIZ 14

## 8

**The Cold War was called this because...**
a. It was between two snowy countries
b. No shots were fired
c. It took place in the winter

## 9

**What is a bayonet?**
a. A type of aircraft
b. A blade attached to a rifle
c. A net used to catch mines under the sea

## 10

**Germany's V2 rocket, the first object ever sent by humans into outer space, was fuelled using which odd ingredient?**
a. Potatoes
b. Milk
c. Horse manure

## 11

**What institution was founded after World War II to promote peace and cooperation between countries?**
a. Greenpeace
b. The United Nations
c. The Red Cross

## 12

**What invention, made during the time of the French Revolution, was used by executioners?**
a. Muskets
b. The guillotine
c. The electric chair

## 13

**Jinshin-no-ran was a Japanese civil war fought in the first century AD. What does Jinshin-no-ran translate as?**
a. War of the Month of Apples
b. War of the Year of the Monkey
c. War of the Time of Plenty

## 14

**Which invention, used in wars for centuries, was originally developed as a medicine?**
a. Gunpowder
b. Gasoline
c. Gas masks

## 15

**The world's first electric computer was developed during which war?**
a. World War I
b. World War II
c. Korean War

# THE WORLD AT WAR

## 1

**b. 2.**
Both world wars took place in the 20th century. Advances in technology and political alliances meant that the wars stretched all over the world.

## 2

**a. Controlling England.**
The War of the Roses was a civil war (which means a war within a country, rather than between different countries) that was fought between the House of York and House of Lancaster. The symbol of each of these houses was a rose (red for the Lancasters and white for the Yorks), hence the name of the war.

## 3

**a. World War I.**
Lasting over 4 years, World War I ended in November 1918. It devastated the populations of European countries, with millions of military and civilians killed during the fighting.

## 4

**b. Human skin.**
The throne's cushion was covered in human skin! As well as this, it had brass knobs that were shaped like human skulls.

## 5

**b. Pigeons.**
Pigeons were trained to carry messages from the front lines of battle to the headquarters. The Germans, on the other side, trained hawks to kill the pigeons.

## 6

**a. Storm.**
The Gulf War spilled over from the 1990s into the 21st century and led to the Iraqi government and its leader, Saddam Hussein, being overthrown.

## 7

**a. The Crimean War.**
This was a war fought between Russia and an alliance of Britain, France, Turkey and Sardinia. They wanted to stop Russia expanding its territory.

## 8

**b. No shots were fired.**
Because bombs had been invented that, if used by either side, could destroy most life on Earth, it was too risky to start.

## 9

**b. A blade attached to a rifle.**
Bayonets were originally knives stuck to the end of rifle that were used by hunters.

## 10

**a. Potatoes.**
Although the rocket's creator, Wehner von Braun, worked for the Nazis, after the war he went on to help design the rockets that would take humans to the moon!

## 11

**b. The United Nations.**
The flags of all 193 members of the United Nations fly outside its headquarters in New York, USA.

## 12

**b. The guillotine.**
By inventing the guillotine, the execution process was a quicker and cleaner way for the executioner to carry out their duties.

## 13

**b. War of the Year of the Monkey.**
The war happened as two people wanted to be the Japanese emperor. The loser, Ōtomo, escaped but strangled himself to death!

## 14

**a. Gunpowder.**
Gunpowder was invented by monks in China, who were looking to find the elixir of life.

## 15

**b. World War II.**
The Colossus computers (there ended up being quite a few of them) were huge machines dedicated to breaking the codes of the Nazis during World War II.

# AMERICAN HISTORY

**1**

**What was American President Abraham Lincoln's nickname?**

a. Sinkin' Lincoln
b. Awesome Abraham
c. Honest Abe

**2**

**Who were the first people to build cities in the Americas?**

a. Native North Americans
b. The Mayans
c. The Europeans

**3**

**Barack Obama, 44th president of the United States, was born in which state?**

a. New York
b. Hawaii
c. Illinois

**4**

**The Constitution of the United States has many additions, called amendments. What did the 18th Amendment do?**

a. Prohibited the sale of alcohol
b. Ended slavery
c. Prohibited public speaking

**5**

**Which famous battle between the US and an alliance of Native American nations is also known as 'Custer's Last Stand'?**

a. The Battle of Gettysburg
b. The Battle of Los Angeles
c. The Battle of Little Bighorn

6

**1881 was a big year for the Wild West. A famous shoot-out happened in Tombstone, Arizona. How is it better known?**

a. The Gunfight at the O.K. Corral
b. The Gunfight at the So-So Corral
c. The Gunfight at the J.K. Corral

7

**Which famous campaigner proclaimed 'I have a dream' to a crowd of 250,000 people at a march on Washington?**

a. Malcolm X
b. Martin Luther King
c. Rosa Parks

8

**In 1929, the Wall Street Crash sent the US into a state of economic crisis, in which many people lost their jobs. What was this known as?**

a. The Great Depression
b. The Large Hole
c. The Starving Times

9

**Who attacked the US at Pearl Harbor in 1941?**

a. The Germans
b. The Japanese
c. The Canadians

10

**Which US President inspired the creation of the name 'Teddy Bear'?**

a. Theodore Roosevelt
b. Grover Cleveland
c. Franklin T. Bear

**DID YOU KNOW?**

In 1792, architects entered a competition to design the White House.

# AMERICAN HISTORY

1

**c. Honest Abe.**

Abraham Lincoln was the 16th President of the United States and was in power during the American Civil War.

2

**b. The Mayans.**

The Mayan and Olmec cultures built cities hundreds of years before the arrival of Columbus and the European settlers.

3

**b. Hawaii.**

Barack Obama was born in the state capital of Honolulu in 1961. He is the only US president born outwith the US mainland.

4

**a. Prohibited the sale of alcohol.**

The Prohibition era in the US lasted from 1920 to 1933 after congress proposed another Constitutional Amendment to cancel out the 18th Amendment.

5

**c. The Battle of Little Bighorn.**

Part of the Great Sioux War, in which Native Americans resisted forced relocation by the US government, the Battle of Little Bighorn was a massive defeat for the US Army, under the leadership of Lt Colonel George Armstrong Custer.

**6**

**a. The Gunfight at the O.K. Corral.**

The gunfight, between a group of lawmen and cattle ranchers, left three of the ranchers dead. The whole thing only lasted 30 seconds.

**7**

**b. Martin Luther King.**

Martin Luther King's dream was that people of different races could live together in harmony. In 1964, the Civil Rights Act was passed, which made segregation (keeping people of different colours apart) and discrimination illegal.

**8**

**a. The Great Depression.**

The thing that crashed was the stock market. A stock market is a place where people buy and sell little bits of companies and businesses. The consequences of the economic crisis affected countries all over the world.

**9**

**b. The Japanese.**

353 Japanese planes made a surprise bombing attack on the US Naval base at Pearl Harbor, in Hawaii. This prompted the US to join the Allied forces in World War II.

**10**

**a. Theodore Roosevelt.**

After seeing a cartoon that showed the president refusing to shoot a bear, a candy shop owner decided to make a new stuffed toy he called the 'Teddy's bear'

**DID YOU KNOW?**

George Washington was the first president of the USA.

# VICTORIANS

## TRUE or FALSE

**1**

The Victorian period was in the 18th century.

**2**

Victoria was only 2 years old when she became Queen.

**3**

The Victorian serial killer, Jack the Ripper was never caught.

**4**

Queen Victoria was less than 5 feet tall.

**5**

Queen Victoria had 12 children.

**6**

Many Victorian children were made to work.

**7**

Queen Victoria was married to her first cousin.

**8**

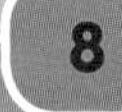

Queen Victoria was the longest reining British monarch.

**9**

The telephone, bicycle, typewriter, motor car and movies were all invented in the Victorian era.

**10**

Queen Victoria made education compulsory.

**11**

A number of games, such as rugby, were invented.

**12**

The Victorian era saw the dawn of aeroplanes: human-powered flight.

**13**

Queen Victoria was the first person to be shown on a postage stamp.

**14**

One of Queen Victoria's children studied under the famous nurse, Florence Nightingale.

**15**

One of the world's greatest waterfalls is named after Queen Victoria.

**DID YOU KNOW?**

In Victorian times, pineapples were a symbol of wealth.

# VICTORIANS

## TRUE or FALSE

**1**

FALSE.
The Victorian era was during the reign of Queen Victoria, lasting from 20 June 1837 until 22 January 1901.

**2**

FALSE.
Victoria was 18 when she was crowned.

**3**

TRUE.
Even today, people try to figure out exactly who was responsible for the series of murders that took place in the Whitechapel area of London.

**4**

TRUE.
Queen Victoria was only 1.52 metres in height – 10 cm less than current monarch Queen Elizabeth II.

**5**

FALSE.
She did have nine children though, including a future queen of Germany as well as the next King of England!

**6**

TRUE.
Making children work is bad enough but many of them had dangerous jobs such as working in mines or cleaning chimneys.

**7**

TRUE.
Victoria loved Albert dearly. The Albert Hall in London is named after him.

**8**

FALSE.
Queen Victoria was the longest reigning monarch until her great-great-grandaughter Queen Elizabeth II, surpassed her.

## 9

**TRUE.**
Methods for the mass production of steel were also invented, which meant that ships, bridges and buildings could be made on a much bigger scale.

## 10

**TRUE.**
Queen Victoria believed that education was vital for all children (not just those who could afford the fees).

## 11

**TRUE.**
The Victorians' love of games, such as rugby, football and cricket, spread across the whole empire.

## 12

**FALSE.**
The Wright Brothers' famous first flight happened in 1903.

## 13

**TRUE.**
This was the famous 'penny black' stamp, which is now prized by stamp collectors all over the world.

## 14

**TRUE.**
Alice was a caring daughter with an interest in medicine and healthcare. She made bandages and, during times of war, visited the injured in hospital.

### DID YOU KNOW?

**'Broxy' was the name given to diseased meat that was sold by butchers in Victorian times.**

## 15

**TRUE.**
Victoria Falls sits between Zimbabwe and Zambia. Its local name is Mosi-oa-Tunya which means 'the smoke that thunders'. At one point, the falls are over one mile wide with water falling over 100 m (350 feet) down.

# AZTECS AND INCAS

## 1

**What is Machu Picchu?**

a. An ancient Incan city
b. An ancient Mayan sports ground
c. An ancient Incan name for the sea

## 2

**The Aztec people were attacked by an invading force from which European country?**

a. Spain
b. Portugal
c. Denmark

## 3

**How many people lived in the Aztec Empire?**

a. Half a million
b. 1 million
c. Over 3 million

## 4

**In which modern city is the ancient Aztec capital of Tenochtitlàn located?**

a. Mexico City
b. Guadalajara
c. Acapulco

## 5

**The Aztec people believed that there had been a number of failed Earths before this one. Which one did they think they were living in?**

a. The fifth
b. The fiftieth
c. The hundredth

## 6

**The Aztecs had many gods. Their god of rain and water was called...**

a. Malloch b. Tlaloc
c. Brolli

## 7

**What did the Incas use to record information?**

a. Scratches on soft stone
b. Collections of dried kidney beans
c. Knots in a rope

## 8

**What cosmic event did the Aztec think threatened pregnancy?**

a. Solar eclipse
b. Comet
c. Star alignment

## 9

**The best of the best warriors in the Aztec empire were known by which furry and feathered names?**

a. The tigers and the falcons
b. The jaguars and the eagles
c. The leopards and the hawks

## 10

**What did the parents of Aztec children do to help them grow up?**

a. They tickled their feet with feathers
b. They pulled on their heads to stretch their necks
c. They gave them special medicines

## 11

**What insects did the Aztecs consider to be a bad omen?**

a. Spiders b. Ants
c. Beetles

## 12

**Why was this hairless breed of dog considered to be a very important companion in Aztec culture?**

a. It was a guide to the underworld
b. It had lightning in its bones
c. It could turn invisible

## 13

**The Inca started off in Peru, but at its height, the civilisation stretched down the western edge of the South American continent as far as...**

a. Brazil
b. Mexico
c. Chile

## 14

**What is remarkable about the way the buildings and walls are built in Machu Picchu?**

a. They don't use any mortar to stick the bricks together
b. The bricks were made by aliens
c. The walls are incredibly thin

## 15

**How long did people live at Machu Picchu?**

a. 300 years
b. 200 years
c. 100 years

# AZTECS AND INCAS

## 1

**a. An ancient Incan city.**

The ruins of the ancient city of Machu Picchu (whose name means 'Old Peak' in the local language) sits on top of a mountain that's 2,438 m (nearly 8,000 feet) tall!

## 2

**a. Spain.**

Hernán Cortés, who led the conquering Spanish force, is said to have destroyed 10 of his ships to stop a rebelling force in his army from fleeing.

## 3

**c. Over 3 million.**

The empire covered over 200,000 square km of land and many different languages were spoken throughout the different states.

## 4

**a. Mexico City.**

The ruins are actually right in the heart of modern-day Mexico's capital city.

## 5

**a. The fifth.**

They called the four failed worlds that had gone before 'failed suns' and they named their time the time of the 'fifth sun.'

## 6

**b. Tlaloc.**

Other Aztec gods included Huitzilopochtli, their god of war, and Coatlicue, the goddess of life and death.

## 7

**c. Knots in a rope.**

These coloured cords were called quipus.

## 8

**a. Solar eclipse.**

The Aztecs believed that their astral deities turned into monsters when the sun was covered, and that they would turn unborn babies into monsters too.

## 9

**b. The jaguars and the eagles.**

The warriors often took captives to offer as human sacrifices at their temples.

## 10

**b. They pulled on their heads to stretch their necks.**

It was believed that by stretching the neck and other body parts like fingers and legs, proper growth would be achieved.

## 11

**b. Ants.**

The Aztecs had many superstitions, but it probably isn't a great thing to have a nest of ants in your house.

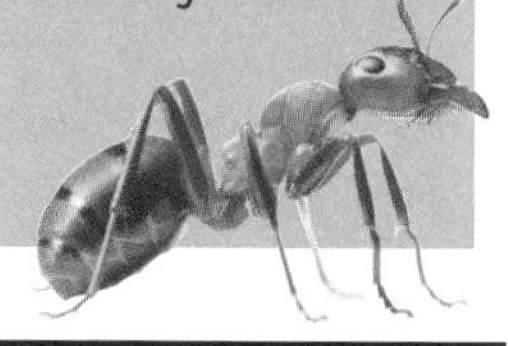

## 12

**a. It was a guide to the underworld.**

This is one of the most ancient breeds of dog in the world.

## 13

**c. Chile.**

At one point, the Incan civilisation stretched over 4,000 km (2,500 miles) down the side of the continent. That's about the same distance as from the east to the west coast of the United States!

## 14

**a. They don't use any mortar to stick the bricks together.**

To build a city out of stones that are so precisely cut and placed that they don't need any mortar to keep them together is an amazing feat, especially in the 1400s.

## 15

**c. 100 years.**

Amazingly, after only 100 years, the Incas abandoned the city. Nobody knows exactly why they did this.

**DID YOU KNOW?**

**Aztecs didn't use an alphabet, instead they used pictures to communicate.**

# Incredible CREATURES

**TARANTULAS** periodically shed their **SKELETONS** – and **REPLACE** their **INTERNAL ORGANS.**

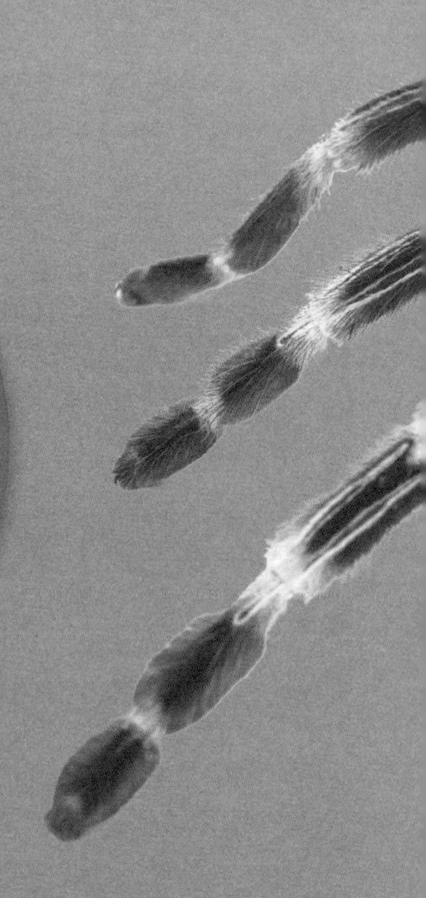

# CATEGORY 3

# MAMMALS

**1** **How many spines does a European hedgehog have?**
a. 1,000 b. 3,000 c. 5,000

**2** **What are you likely to find growing on a sloth?**
a. Algae b. Mould c. Spikes

**3** **Which bear likes to eat bamboo?**
a. Pandas b. Polar bears c. Sun bears

**4** **Which mammal is the largest animal on Earth?**
a. Elephant b. Giraffe c. Blue whale

**5** **Why do echidnas have backward-pointing feet?**
a. To increase speed
b. To aid digging
c. To move sideways

**6** **Where would you expect to find reindeers?**
a. The Arctic b. The Antarctic c. The Sahara

**7** **Which animals would you expect to live in a warren?**
a. Badgers b. Rabbits c. Meerkats

# QUIZ 18

**8** **To which continent are snow leopards native?**
a. North America b. Europe c. Asia

**9** **Which habitat do meerkats live in?**
a. Forests b. Deserts c. Jungles

**10** **Which animal are okapis most like?**
a. Zebras
b. Giraffes
c. Horses

**11** **Which of these best describes the pygmy shrew?**
a. One of the fastest mammals
b. One of the quietest mammals
c. One of the smallest mammals

**12** **What are baby kangaroos called?**
a. Billys b. Sheilas c. Joeys

**13** **What part of a rat never stops growing?**
a. Front teeth b. Whiskers c. Claws

**14** **What is the largest wild cat in the world?**
a. Snow leopard b. Tiger c. Panther

**DID YOU KNOW?**

**Baby kangaroos are around the size of a grape when they are born.**

# MAMMALS

**1** **c. 5,000.** Each spine is 2–2.5 cm long and cream in colour with a dark band across the middle.

**2** **a. Algae.** The grooves and cracks in sloth hair are suitable for algal colonisation.

**3** **a. Pandas.** Giant pandas eat only bamboo. To survive on such a high-fibre, low-calorie diet, pandas spend all day eating.

**4** **c. Blue whale.** They can grow up to 30 metres long. Their tongues alone can weigh as much as an elephant and their hearts, as much as a horse.

**5** **b. To aid digging.** Echidnas are diggers. They use their backward-pointing feet to remove soil.

**6** **a. The Arctic.** Reindeers live in the Arctic tundra and forests of Greenland, Scandinavia, Russia, Alaska and Canada.

**7** **b. Rabbits.** They live in warrens – a series of tunnels and rooms that they dig underground.

**8** **c. Asia.** Twelve countries have snow leopards, such as China and Nepal. They are usually found above 3000m; that's over twice the height of Ben Nevis.

**DID YOU KNOW?**

**A meerkat can spot an eagle in flight from more than 300 metres away.**

**9** **b. Deserts.** Meerkats live in the deserts and grasslands of the southern tip of Africa.

**10** **b. Giraffes.** Okapis and giraffes both have bluish black tongues that they use for plucking leaves.

**11** **c. One of the smallest mammals.** Pygmy shrews have a body length of 3.8 to 5 cm and weigh as little as 2 grams.

**12** **c. Joeys.** Female kangaroos sport a pouch on their belly, made by a fold in the skin, to cradle their joeys.

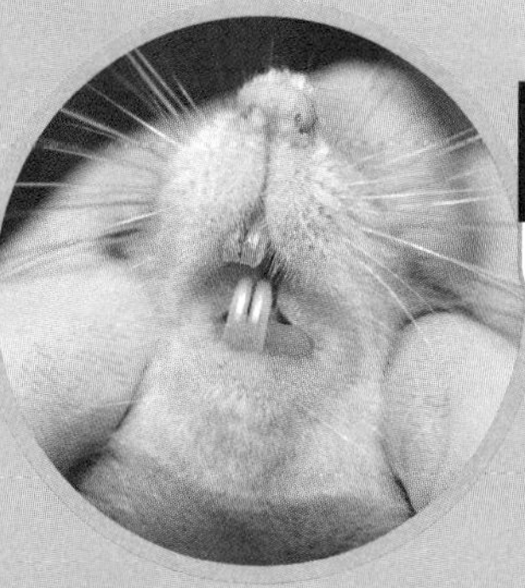

**13** **a. Front teeth.** Rats have to keep nibbling on food to wear their front teeth down, otherwise eating would be impossible!

**14** **b. Tiger.** Adult tigers can weigh up to 300 kg – that's about the same as ten 9-year-olds!

# BIRDS

**1**

**What is another name for a bird of prey?**

a. Raptor
b. Viper
c. Beakclaw

**2**

**Which bird is traditionally associated with wisdom?**

a. Falcon
b. Owl
c. Robin

**3**

**What is the most common species of bird in the world?**

a. Seagull
b. Pigeon
c. Chicken

**4**

**Which species of bird has the largest wingspan in the world?**

a. Condor
b. Bald eagle
c. Albatross

**5**

**Which of these is modelled on the shape of a bird's wing?**

a. Aeroplane wing
b. Surfboard
c. Helicopter blade

**6**

**How many different living species of bird are there?**

a. 3,000
b. 10,000
c. 30,000

**7**

**Which of the following is *not* a type of flightless bird?**

a. Ostrich
b. Penguin
c. Hummingbird

**8**

**How many birds do you end up with at the end of the song 'The Twelve Days of Christmas'?**

a. 24
b. 72
c. 184

## 9

**Which of these is the fastest bird in the air?**

a. Golden eagle
b. Peregrine falcon
c. Flamingo

## 10

**Crows are said to have the intelligence age of a:**

a. One-year-old
b. Four-year-old
c. Seven-year-old

## 11

**What type of bird lays its eggs in another bird's nest?**

a. Cuckoo
b. Cardinal
c. Grebe

## 12

**Which part of a pelican is the largest of all birds?**

a. Feet
b. Bill
c. Wings

## 13

**Which of these terms came from hunting birds?**

a. Sniper
b. Bait
c. Commando

## 14

**Which species of bird has a diet mainly made up of bones?**

a. Hawks b. Vultures
c. Sparrows

# BIRDS

## 1

**a. Raptor.**

Birds of prey come in all sizes. The smallest is called the falconet.

## 2

**b. Owl.**

The tradition of believing owls to be wise goes back to the Ancient Greeks and the goddess Athena.

## 3

**c. Chicken.**

The chicken comes out on top when it comes to sheer numbers as there are around 23 billion of them. But most of these birds are reared to be eaten.

## 4

**c. Albatross.**

These seabirds have wingspans of up to 3.3 m (nearly 11 feet) that they use to glide over the oceans of the southern hemisphere.

## 5

**a. Aeroplane wing.**

Birds' wings have evolved to give them lift: the leading edge of the wing is thick, with the back edge tapering to a point.

## 6

**b. 10,000.**

Different bird species have adapted to habitats all over the world. They vary from the penguins living on the Antarctic ice-cap, to birds of paradise in the hot, humid rainforests.

## 7

**c. Hummingbird.**

Hummingbirds are able to hover and move forwards and backwards with incredible precision. The bee hummingbird is the smallest species of bird in the world.

# QUIZ 19 ANSWERS

## 8

**c. 184.**

By day 7 (seven swans a-swimming), you'd be getting 23 birds per day: seven swans, six geese, four calling birds, three French hens, two turtle doves, and a partridge in a pear tree.

## 9

**b. Peregrine falcon.**

Peregrine falcons hunt by climbing high into the air and then diving down towards their prey.

## 10

**c. Seven.**

Crows have been seen to use tools to solve problems, to hold grudges and to enjoy playing around. These are all signs of intelligence.

## 11

**a. Cuckoo.**

Cuckoos are 'brood parasites' - the mother cuckoo lays her egg in the nest of a smaller bird. She sometimes even pushes the host's own egg out of the nest!

## 12

**b. Bill.**

The bill of the Australian Pelicaan can be up to half a metre (50 cm, or 20 inches) long. The pelican scoops up a bill full of water then strains the water out, leaving fish to eat.

## 13

**a. Sniper.**

Snipes – a chubby little bird that is amazingly fast in the air – were traditionally very hard to hunt. Those who succeeded were called 'snipers' in recognition of their abilities with a rifle.

## 14

**b. Vulture.**

Bearded vultures have a diet of up to 90% bone. They drop the bones onto stony ground so that they shatter. The birds can then eat the nutritious marrow inside as well as the bone fragments.

# REPTILES

1

**Which reptile is known for changing the colour of its skin?**

a. Gila monster
b. Komodo dragon
c. Chameleon

2

**What is the largest species of reptile in the world?**

a. Gila monster
b. Komodo dragon
c. Monitor lizard

3

**Which type of reptile lives the longest?**

a. Tortoise
b. Alligator
c. Crocodile

4

**What do snakes use to taste and smell the air?**

a. Special senses under their eyes
b. Their forked tongue, which they flick out
c. Their tails, which swoop through the environment

5

**How does a constrictor snake kill its prey?**

a. Through venom in its fangs
b. Through crushing it by squeezing
c. Through slapping it with its tail

6

**What is the largest snake in the world?**

a. King cobra
b. Black mamba
c. Green anaconda

7

**What is the scientific name of the top shell of a tortoise or turtle?**

a. Pastron
b. Carapace
c. Abdomen

8

**What is the collective noun for tortoises?**

a. A tiptoe
b. A creep
c. A shimmy

9

**Where in the world are marine iguanas found?**

a. The Galapagos Islands
b. The Maldives
c. The Bahamas

10

**Which lizard is famous for being able to walk on water?**

a. Nile monitor lizard
b. Basilisk lizard
c. Bearded dragon

11

**This is a chuckwalla (below). When threatened by a predator, what does it do?**

a. Spits a venom at the predator's eyes
b. Buries its head in the sand
c. Puffs up its body to wedge itself between rocks

12

**How does a Texas horned lizard protect itself when it feels threatened?**

a. It sprints away on its front legs
b. It spits lots of its blood out through its eyes
c. It opens its mouth wide and runs at the attacker

13

**Terrapins are a type of what?**

a. Turtle
b. Snake
c. Lizard

14

**Which type of snake can 'stand up', lifting about a third of itself up. It can also fan out its neck into a 'hood' to intimidate its attacker.**

a. Cobra
b. Viper
c. Python

## DID YOU KNOW?

**Terrapins once delayed dozens of flights from New York when they crossed the runway to lay eggs in the airport grounds.**

# REPTILES

**1**

**c. Chameleon.**

In addition to being able to change colour, the chameleon also has eyes that can move independently, to track two different prey, but then switch to focus on one when the chameleon decides which looks tastier.

**2**

**b. Komodo dragon.**

These real-life dragons can grow up to 3 m (10 feet) in length. They hunt by delivering a bite that poisons their prey (which can be as large as a water buffalo). The dragons then follow the bitten animal as it succumbs to deadly blood poisoning.

**3**

**a. Tortoise.**

In 2020, Jonathan, the oldest surviving tortoise will reach 188.

**4**

**b. Their forked tongues, which they flick out.**

Some snakes also have another sense, that allows them to see body heat!

**5**

**b. Through crushing it by squeezing.**

Boa constrictors wait to ambush their prey and then squeeze them in the coils of their body; to cut of their blood supply before swallowing them whole.

**6**

**c. Green anaconda.**

Anacondas grow up to 9 metres long – that's as long as six 10-year-olds laid end to end!

**7**

**b. Carapace.**

The shells of turtles and tortoises are very protective. However, this protection comes at a cost: both turtles and tortoises have to use their legs to help them breathe!

# QUIZ 20 ANSWERS

**8**

**b. A creep.**

A female giant Galapagos tortoise of a species believed to be extinct for 100 years has been discovered in a remote location. She is more than 100 years old.

**9**

**a. The Galapagos Islands.**

The Galapagos Islands straddle the equator and are very remote. This has led to lots of different species of animal living there.

**10**

**b. Basilisk lizard.**

Basilisk lizards live in Latin America, from Mexico down to northern Colombia. When they're threatened, they can drop onto the water and run on its surface.

**11**

**c. Puffs up its body to wedge itself between rocks.**

These lizards live in Mexico and the USA. They are herbivores, meaning they don't eat meat.

**12**

**b. It spits lots of its blood out through its eyes.**

This lizard has horns all over its head and has two lines of frilled scales along its sides. It is one of a group of lizards also known as the horny toads.

**13**

**a. Turtle.**

Terrapins tend to live in freshwater ponds, rivers and lakes. They are sometimes found in slightly salty (or brackish) waters.

**14**

**a. Cobra.**

King cobras can reach 5.5 metres (18 feet) in length – they are the longest of all venomous snakes.

**DID YOU KNOW?**

**King cobras are naturally shy and only become aggressive when provoked.**

# FISH

**1** **What is the fastest shark in the sea?**
a. Hammerhead shark b. Shortfin mako shark c. Great white shark

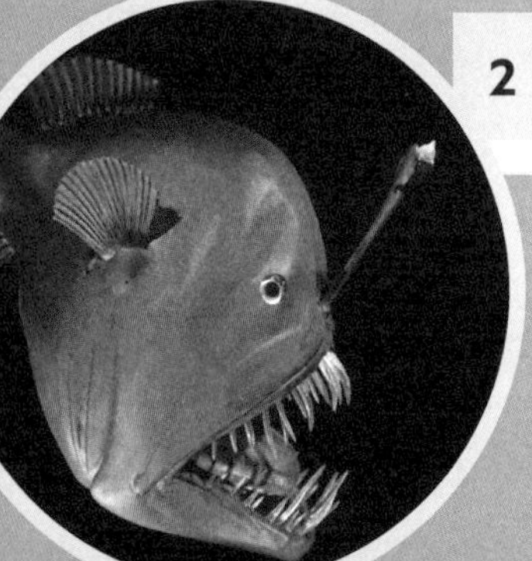

**2** **Which deep sea fish has a long bit of bone that sticks out in front of their heads like a fishing pole?**
a. Angler fish b. Fishing fish c. Sailor fish

**3** **Which fish is the largest in the world?**
a. Orca b. Whale shark c. Basking shark

**4** **How does a fish breathe underwater?**
a. By popping up to the surface b. Using gills
c. Using their dorsal fins

**5** **Why does a parrotfish have teeth outside its jaws?**
a. To be able to crunch up coral
b. To be able to crunch up other parrotfish
c. To be able to crunch up seaweed

**6** **How many species of fish are there in the world?**
a. 12,000 b. 22,000 c. 32,000

**7** **The scales of a fish have 'rings'. What do these rings do?**
a. Tell us how old the fish is b. Help the fish glide through the water
c. Help the fish absorb oxygen

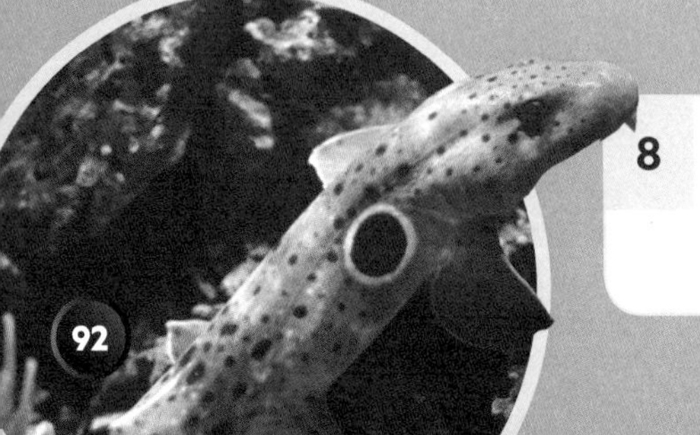

**8** **An epaulette shark has spots on its shoulders. It is also famous for what?**
a. Turning its stomach inside out to feed
b. Walking along the sea floor using its fins
c. Biting larger fish and hitching a ride

**9** **To what family of fish does this sawfish (above) belong?**
a. Rays b. Salmon c. Seahorses

**10** **What type of fish is this (right)?**
a. Sunfish b. Lionfish c. Clownfish

**11** **What is the most poisonous fish in the world?**
a. Stonefish b. Toadfish c. Frogfish

**12** **Which fish is born without teeth and unable to see? It makes a burrow in the riverbed and stays there for up to seven years.**
a. Moray eel b. Lamprey c. Tuna

**DID YOU KNOW?**

**Fossils suggest that fish have been on Earth for more than 500 million years.**

**13** **What type of fish is this (right)?**
a. Sealion b. Seahorse c. Seamule

**14** **What is a group of fish called?**
a. A college b. A school
c. A university

# FISH

**1** **b. Shortfin mako shark.** These speedy sharks can swim at up to 74 kmph (45 mph).

**2** **a. Angler fish.** Their bony lure has a light at the end. The light is created by millions of luminescent bacteria that live in this part of the fish.

**3** **b. Whale shark.** These shy but huge fish are filter feeders. This means they get their food by sieving through the water to pick out tiny creatures like krill.

**4** **b. Using gills.** All fish use gills to breathe under-water. These pick up oxygen as the water flows through them. They also release carbon dioxide.

**5** **a. To be able to crunch up coral.** Parrotfish crunch the coral down to get to the algae hidden inside. Their poo is sand: all the broken up bits of coral that they can't digest.

**6** **c. 32,000.** The range of fish species is staggering, but understandable given that 70% of the planet's surface is covered with water.

**7** **a. Tell us how old the fish is.** Just like the rings of a tree trunk, the ridge lines on a fish's scales can tell us how old the fish is.

**8** **b. Walking along the sea floor using its fins.** Epaulette sharks like to walk rather than swim when hunting. They live in oxygen-depleted rock pools and can be seen 'walking' from pool to pool.

**9** **a. Rays.** These intimidating creatures use their elongated snout (called a rostrum) to attack their prey. The teeth along its edge aren't teeth at all; they are specially adapted scales.

**10** **b. Lionfish.** Red lionfish are flamboyantly coloured and shaped, acting as camouflage in the reefs where it lives and hunts. Some of the spines contain venom which are used for defence.

**11** **a. Stonefish.** The stonefish does not use its venom-filled spines to attack its prey; it is an ambush predator that pretends to be a stone in the sand. When an unsuspecting fish swims by, the stonefish strikes in around a hundredth of a second.

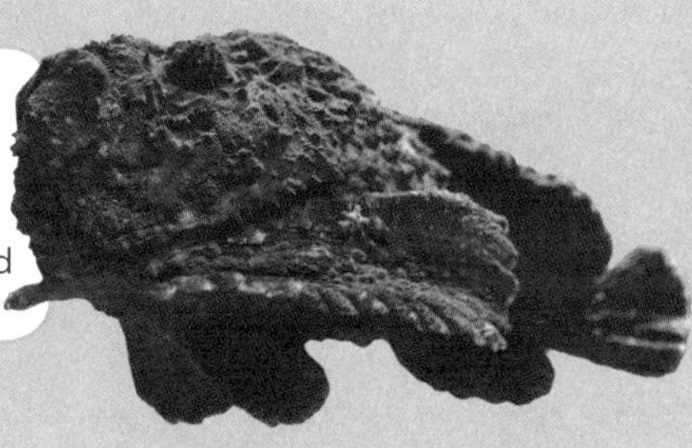

**12** **b. Lamprey.** These fish are bloodsuckers. When they emerge fully grown, their gill holes work and they have ring upon ring of circular teeth. They even have tooth-like structures on their tongue!

**13** **b. Seahorse.** There are over 50 species of seahorse that we know of.

**14** **b. A school.** Fish travel together as there is safety in numbers: they are less likely to be eaten.

# AMPHIBIANS

**1**

**The word 'amphibian' comes from which language?**

a. Greek
b. Latin
c. French

**2**

**Which one of these can break their own toe-bones and push them through the skin to make claws?**

a. Sleek salamander
b. African hairy frog
c. Bearded frog

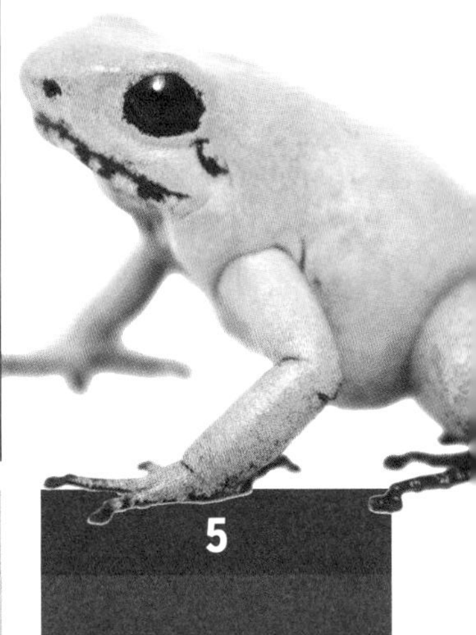

**3**

**What is the largest amphibian in the world?**

a. Giant salamander
b. Bigly toad
c. Notnarrow newt

**4**

**Why are glass frogs named that way?**

a. They can climb up glass
b. They are partly see-through
c. They shatter if dropped

**5**

**What sort of frog is this (above)?**

a. Golden poison frog
b. Yellow sea frog
c. Fire tree frog

**6**

**What are amphibian young called?**

a. Jellyfish
b. Tadpoles
c. Wigworms

**7**

**What amphibian caused havoc across northern Australia in the 1930s and 40s?**

a. Cane toad
b. Stick frog
c. Pole salamander

## 8

**What kind of amphibian is this?**

a. Lungfish
b. Axolotl
c. Grouper

## 9

**How long does it take the bullfrog tadpole to mature and become a frog?**

a. 2 years
b. 2 weeks
c. 2 days

## 10

**Why do frogs close their eyes when they eat?**

a. Because they don't like looking at their food
b. It helps them eat
c. Their brains are too small to cope with seeing and eating at the same time

## 11

**What do most amphibians have between their eyes?**

a. A horn
b. Another eye
c. Dots and splotches

## 12

**What kind of amphibian is this (right)?**

a. Mudskipper
b. Sandslipper
c. Beach-hopper

## 13

**What's so special about the Alaskan wood frog?**

a. Its skin hardens into a thick crust
b. It can stop its heart beating for weeks
c. Its belch can kill beetles and ants

## 14

**What type of amphibian is a newt?**

a. Caecilian
b. Toad
c. Salamander

# AMPHIBIANS

## 1

**a. Greek.**

The word translates as 'living a double life'– indicating the fact that amphibians need to live both in and out of the water.

## 2

**b. African hairy frog.**

You would not want to mess with this frog!

## 3

**a. Giant salamander.**

This amphibian can grow to nearly 2 metres (6 feet) and, when mature, can weigh up to 50 kg.

## 4

**b. They are partly see-through.**

These South American frogs have translucent skin on their abdomens that shows the heart, liver and intestines.

## 5

**a. Golden poison frog.**

These tiny frogs are only around 2 to 5 cm in length but each has enough venom on its skin to kill 10 humans.

## 6

**b. Tadpoles.**

Tadpoles tend to be grouped together in clumps of spawn. As they grow, they lose their tails and develop limbs.

## 7

**a. Cane toad.**

3,000 cane toads were released into northern Australia in 1935. The hope was that they would control the cane beetle population that was destroying crops. However, the cane toad became the problem as they multiplied and their numbers grew into the millions.

# QUIZ 22 ANSWERS

## 8

**b. Axolotl.**

These creatures do not fully develop from their 'tadpole' phase: they retain the external frilly gills and dorsal fin that runs down their spine.

## 9

**a. 2 years.**

Female bullfrogs can lay up to 20,000 eggs. These float as frogspawn on top of a pond or lake.

## 10

**b. It helps them eat.**

Frogs' neck muscles are weak so they pull their eyes down into their heads to help push the food along.

## 11

**b. Another eye.**

It's true! Most amphibians have this third eye (called the parietal eye). It is hidden under a layer of skin but detects light and dark and helps to regulate the amphibians' waking and sleeping patterns.

## 12

**a. Mudskipper.**

Some species of mudskippers don't only walk on mudflats, they also climb trees.

## 14

**c. Salamander.**

The great crested newt is called that because males develop a crinkly crest along their backs. They are also known as 'warty newts.'

## 13

**b. It can stop its heart beating.**

In the harsh Arctic winters, the tree frog covers itself with a couple of inches of leaves and then freezes like the rest of the environment around it. Up to 60% of the frog—including its heart—totally freezes, then thaws as the weather gets warmer.

# INVERTEBRATES

**1**

**What percentage of the world's animal population doesn't have a spine?**

a. 35%
b. 76%
c. 97%

**2**

**Where do you find leafcutter ants?**

a. The Amazon Rainfroest
b. The Sahara Desert
c. The Scottish Highlands

**3**

**What is a type of coral, that kind of looks like deer antlers?**

a. Staghorn coral
b. Doetlers coral
c. Moose coral

**4**

**There are more species of this kind of invertebrate than any other creature. Which is it?**

a. Ant
b. Beetle
c. Spider

**5**

**What type of butterfly makes an annual migration from Canada to Mexico?**

a. Monarch butterfly
b. King butterfly
c. Prince butterfly

**6**

**Which of these invertebrates drinks nectar and eats and collects pollen?**

a. Spiders
b. Bees
c. Butterflies

**7**

**What constitutes an invertebrate creature?**

a. It doesn't have legs
b. It doesn't have a spine
c. It doesn't need to breathe

**8**

**What is a bee's home called?**

a. A nest
b. A pad
c. A block

9

**What is this invertebrate (above)?**

a. A scorpion
b. A bumblebee
c. A tarantula

10

**Which invertebrate is responsible for building these strange structures (right)?**

a. Ants
b. Wasps
c. Termites

11

**Which of these invertebrates are used to cure diseases?**

a. Leeches
b. Slugs
c. Snails

12

**What invertebrate is this (below)?**

a. Cicada
b. Praying mantis
c. Grasshopper

13

**How many eyes does a grasshopper have?**

a. 4
b. 5
c. 6

14

**Which of these invertebrates is a popular dish in France?**

a. Ants
b. Snails
c. Butterflies

# INVERTEBRATES

**1**

**c. 97%.**

Instead of having backbones, some invertebrates have used protein fibres to construct skeletons.

**2**

**c. The Amazon Rainforest.**

Leafcutter ants can be found in the tropical rainforests and semi-tropical forests of South America, Central America and southern North America.

**3**

**a. Staghorn coral.**

Staghorn coral can grow more than 5 cm (2 inches) per year. However, global warming is contributing to the destruction of the coral's reef habitat.

**4**

**b. Beetle.**

Beetles tend to have strong biting jaws. In fact, the word 'beetle' comes from an old Anglo-Saxon word 'bitan' that means 'to bite'.

**5**

**a. Monarch butterfly.**

Thanks to changes to their habitat (humans removing milkweed from their fields), monarch butterfly populations have plummeted over 90% since the 1980s.

**6**

**b. Bees.**

Flying from flower to flower, bees pollinate the plants around them.

**7**

**b. It doesn't have a spine.**

This category covers a lot of different species: from butterflies to slugs and from spiders to dragonflies.

**8**

**a. A nest.**

Bees live in nests, however, there are over 250 species of bee that live alone. These are known as 'solitary bees'.

**9**

**c. A tarantula.**

There are over 40,000 species of spider. Tarantulas are some of the largest. The Goliath birdeater tarantula has a leg-span of 30 cm (nearly 1 foot).

**10**

**c. Termites.**

Millions of termites, working together, dig up dirt and build these magnificent structures filled with tunnels and chambers. They can be over 5 metres (16 feet) tall!

**11**

**a. Leeches.**

Leeches have been used in medicine for over 2,000 years. People used to believe that many diseases were the result of having too much blood.

**12**

**b. Praying mantis.**

Females sometimes decapitate their partners whilst mating. Then they eat the male.

**DID YOU KNOW?**

**A praying mantins can swivel its eyes 180°.**

**13**

**b. 5.**

Grasshoppers have two large eyes and three smaller ones. The larger eyes allow grasshoppers to see all around them.

**14**

**b. Snails.**

In France, these are called 'escargot' and are cooked, often with parsley and butter.

# UNDER THE SEA

**1** **Which of these is a difference between an octopus and a squid?**
a. An octopus has two eyes; a squid has four eyes
b. An octopus has eight arms; a squid has eight arms and two tentacles
c. An octopus has one beak; a squid has eight small beaks

**2** **Which of these animals that live under the sea used to walk on land?**
a. Whale b. Jellyfish c. Manta ray

**3** **What are sponges classified as?**
a. Plants b. Fungi c. Animals

**4** **What is the largest invertebrate animal in the world?**
a. Dumbo squid b. Giant squid c. Stingray

**5** **What type of starfish is this (right)?**
a. Crown of thorns starfish
b. Feathered edge starfish
c. Lidgren's starfish

**6** **Which animal is known as 'the Unicorn of the sea'?**
a. Dolphins b. Narwhals c. Walruses

**7** **Which animal can boil the sea with its punch?**
a. Mantis shrimp
b. Tarantula fish
c. Slug starfish

**8** **What type of sea animal is this (left)?**
a. Walrus b. Seal c. Sea lion

**9** **Which mammal dives deeper into the ocean?**
a. Bottlenose dolphin b. Orca c. Sperm whale

**10** **What is the average lifespan of a giant clam?**
a. 10 months b. 10 years c. 100 years

**11** **Which of these is actually a colony of tiny creatures called polyps?**
a. Manta ray b. Oyster c. Portugese man o' war

**12** **What type of crab finds shells and other objects to call home?**
a. Hermit crab
b. Fiddler crab
c. Ghost crab

**13** **What is this mammal (below)? It is the largest creature that we know of (including the dinosaurs).**
a. Sperm whale b. Blue whale c. Humpback whale

**14** **Which of these is the largest breed of dolphin?**
a. Porpoise b. Orca c. Whale shark

**DID YOU KNOW?**

**Dolphins communicate through squeaks, whistles and clicks.**

# UNDER THE SEA

**1** **c. An octopus has eight arms; a squid has eight arms and two tentacles.** There are suckers attached to the ends of the squid's tentacles.

**2** **a. Whale.** The ancestors of whales lived on land around 50 million years ago.

**3** **c. Animals.** Sponges are very simple creatures. They have no organs or nervous system.

**4** **b. Giant squid.** Giant squids really are huge. Their eyes are about as big as a human head (25 cm across).

**5** **a. Crown of thorns starfish.** These pose a threat to coral reefs. The starfish climb up on to the reefs and then turn their stomachs inside out to digest the coral.

**6** **b. Narwhals.** Narwhals have only two teeth. In males, one grows into the horn (which sometimes grow as long as 3 metres, or nearly 10 feet). The other tooth in males, and both teeth in females, do not emerge.

**7** **a. Mantis shrimp.** Mantis shrimps are aggressive relatives of crabs and lobsters. Their punch is so fast that it actually boils the water around the punch.

**8** **a. Walrus.** Walruses use their tusks, which are elongated teeth, to haul themselves up out of the water. They also use them to attack other walruses during the mating season, defence from predators and for foraging on the sea floor.

# QUIZ 24 ANSWERS

**9** **c. Sperm whale.** Sperm whales have been recorded at depths of more than 2,000m (6,500 feet). They also have the largest brain of any known living creature.

**10** **c. 100 years.** Once a giant clam settles on a spot, it stays there for the rest of its life, which can be over 100 years!

**11** **c. Portugese Man o' war.** The long tentacles that drift below the water are painfully venomous.

**12** **a. Hermit crab.** Some hermit crabs are not solitary; they cluster in size order to move into the bigger shell of the clam in front of them in the queue. Sometimes, they form gangs to steal a shell they want from the resident crab and then fight amongst themselves to determine who gets it.

**13** **b. Blue whale.** The tongue of a blue whale can weigh as much as an elephant. It is the biggest animal ever to have existed and yet it eats only small crustaceans, mostly krill.

**14** **b. Orca.** In the wild, orcas move in family groups called 'pods' and hunt their prey with cunning and intelligence.

# IN THE JUNGLE

**1**

**Which of these animals can be found in the jungles of the Congo?**

a. Elephant
b. Arctic fox
c. Alpaca

**2**

**What is the name of this jungle bird (right)?**

a. Emu
b. Cassowary
c. Ostrich

**3**

**Which of these jungle dwellers is our closest genetic relative?**

a. Gorilla
b. Chimpanzee
c. Orangutan

**4**

**Which animal is also known as the puma, the mountain lion and the panther?**

a. Cheetah
b. Lion
c. Cougar

**5**

**Which is the world's largest nocturnal (night living) primate?**

a. Aye aye
b. Tarsier
c. Night monkey

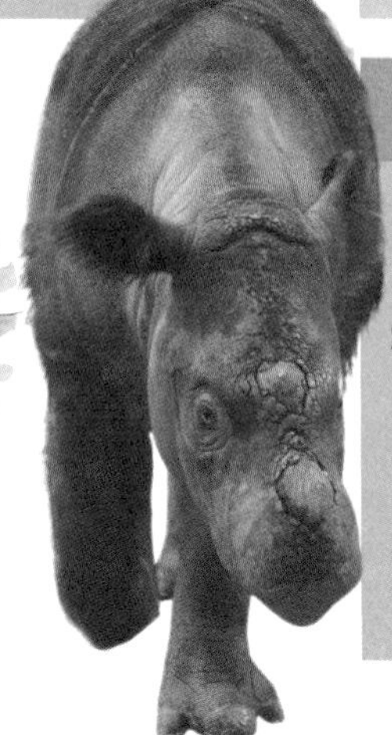

**6**

**What type of animal is this (left)? It lives in Sumatran jungles and is critically endangered?**

a. Sumatran tiger
b. Sumatran rhinoceros
c. Sumatran hippo

**7**

**Jungles are also known as rainforests. How much rain does the Amazon Rainforest receive each year?**

a. Average 500 mm
b. Average 1,000 mm
c. Average 2,000 mm

## 8

**The world's largest rodent lives in the jungles and wetlands of South America. What is it called?**

a. Beaver
b. Coypu
c. Capybara

## 9

**What is the name of this classic red, blue and yellow parrot?**

a. Macaw
b. Macrow
c. Macry

## 10

**Which monkey is famous for its multi-coloured nose?**

a. Bonobo
b. Mandrill
c. Baboon

## 11

**On which continent would you find piranha fish?**

a. Asia
b. South America
c. Africa

## 12

**Which jungle creature's roar can be heard over 3 km (2 miles) away?**

a. Bengal tiger
b. Sun bear
c. Tapir

## 13

**What advantage does the toucan's oversized beak give the bird?**

a. It helpes them to attract a mate
b. It helps them control their body temperature
c. It helps them catch food more effectively

## 14

**What relative of the raccoon was discovered in 2013?**

a. Tarsier
b. Lemur
c. Olinguito

# IN THE JUNGLE

## 1

**a. Elephant.**

These are graceful giants, living in the jungle of the Congo. They are under significant threat from humans who want to kill them for their ivory tusks.

## 2

**b. Cassowary.**

Cassowaries are very dangerous and are able to injure animals, including humans, with their clawed feet.

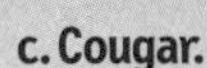

## 3

**b. Chimpanzee.**

With around 98% of the same DNA, chimpanzees are our closest relative.

## 4

**c. Cougar.**

These big cats live in North America and are spread from the Canadian forests to the most southern parts of South America.

## 5

**a. Aye Aye.**

These lemurs live on Madagascar and live and hunt at night. They are the only primate that we believe to use echolocation to find insects within trees.

## 6

**b. Sumatran rhinoceros.**

This is the smallest species of rhino. The Sumatran rhino has darker skin and, unlike other rhino species, has long hair. It is more closely related to their common ancestor the woolly rhino which is extinct.

## 7

**c. Average 2,000 mm.**

The Amazon is an equatorial rainforest and is one of the richest places for biodiversity in the world. It is under threat from human interests that continue to destroy this precious resource.

## 8

**c. Capybara.**

The Capybara is twice as large as a beaver! A rather gross thing that Capybaras do to ensure they are getting the most nutrients from their food is to eat their own poos.

## 9

**a. Macaw.**

Macaws have bones in their tongues that help them to get at the food they eat (nuts and fruits).

## 10

**b. Mandrill.**

Mandrills are the largest of the monkeys and live in the trees of equatorial African rainforests.

## 11

**b. South America.**

Although thought of as being predatory, some types of piranhas have vegetarian diets.

## 12

**a. Bengal tiger.**

In the 20th century, three different populations of tigers became extinct, thanks to humans. Of the five that remain, all are at risk from going extinct.

## 13

**b. It helps them control their body temperature.**

Having a large beak that is filled with air holes and tiny blood vessels enables the toucan to keep cool.

## 14

**c. Olinguito.**

Although it was officially discovered in 2013, many specimens of the Olinguito had been taken, but had been mis-identified.

# IN THE SKY

**1**

**The earliest fossils of this flying creature date back 300 million years. What is it?**

a. Butterfly
b. Moth
c. Dragonfly

**2**

**Where do you find flying lemurs?**

a. Asia
b. Africa
c. Antarctica

**3**

**How far can a flying fish 'fly'?**

a. Nearly 100 m
b. Nearly 250 m
c. Nearly 400 m

**4**

**Which bird uses water, collected in its feathers, to give a drink to its young?**

a. Sandgrouse
b. Drygoose
c. Beachy starling

**5**

**What were the first airborne lifeforms on the planet?**

a. Seeds
b. Hummingbirds
c. Bacteria

**6**

**What is the Draco Lizard better known as?**

a. Flying dragon
b. Flying reptile
c. Gliding geezer

**7**

**Some fruit bats are known as what?**

a. Flying mice
b. Flying foxes
c. Flying rats

**8**

**What does a male red-capped manakin do to impress a female?**

a. Does the 'moonwalk'
b. Does the 'macarena'
c. Does the 'conga'

**9**

**What is this odd looking bird (right)?**

a. Clogbill
b. Shoebill
c. Bootbill

**10**

**What does the Phillipine eagle like to snack on?**

a. Monkeys
b. Deer
c. Insects

**11**

**Which of these sea dwellers is also known to 'fly'?**

a. Shark
b. Squid
c. Tuna

**12**

**How far can a sugar glider fly for?**

a. Over 200 m
b. Over 100 m
c. Over 50 m

# IN THE SKY

1

**c. Dragonfly.**

For the majority of its life, the dragonfly lives in its 'nymph' phase – hunting in the fresh water environments they call home.

2

**a. Asia.**

Colugo, or flying lemurs (below) can't fly, instead they glide through the air.

4

**a. Sandgrouse.**

The male sandgrouse flies to a water hole and rocks back and forth, collecting water in its feathers, that it then gives to its young.

3

**c. Nearly 400 m.**

Flying fish have specially adapted fins that assist them in flying for short distances over the waves. They accelerate to around 60 kilometres per hour (37 miles per hour) to break through the surface of the sea and fly and glide.

5

**c. Bacteria.**

Bacteria, suspended in the air, have likely been around for billions of years.

## QUIZ 26 ANSWERS

**6**

**a. Flying dragon.**

These reptiles have a specially adapted set of ribs, that they can expand to help them glide between branches in the treetops of the jungle.

**7**

**b. Flying foxes.**

Little red flying foxes can fly for nearly 100 km (57 miles) in one night to find food.

**8**

**a. Does the 'moonwalk'.**

Many bird species have elaborate mating rituals. The red-capped manakin dances, shuffling back and forth like Michael Jackson's moonwalk.

**9**

**b. Shoebill.**

This species of pelican has a distinctive bill. It also has a rather strange way of keeping cool: it poos on its own leg!

**10**

**a. Monkeys.**

The Phillipine eagle is the national bird of the Phillipines and is extremely endangered.

**11**

**b. Squid.**

Squid use a jet of water to push them into the air. They fly by gliding, using webs of skin between their tentacles. They can travel around 30 metres (98 feet) per flight.

**12**

**c. Over 50 m.**

Sugar gliders are small nocturnal animals. They fly by using flaps of skin that go from the fourth finger on their front legs to their back ankles.

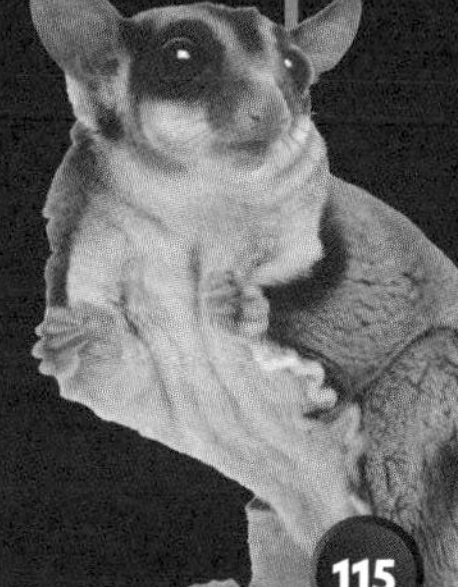

# ACROSS THE DESERT

**1** **What is the difference between a bactrian and a dromedary camel?**

a. The number of humps
b. The size of their feet
c. Their height

**2** **What desert plant is famed for its ability to retain water?**

a. Marram grass
b. Cactus
c. Gorse

**3** **Which desert has recorded the highest temperature?**

a. Atacama Desert
b. Sahara Desert
c. Lut Desert

**4** **Approximately how much of the Earth's surface is taken up by deserts?**

a. 10%
b. 20%
c. 30%

**5** **What type of fox lives in the desert?**

a. Arctic fox b. Fennec fox c. Red fox

**6** **Which of these lives in the Mojave and Sonoran deserts of the USA?**

a. Desert tortoise
b. Oryx
c. Echidna

**7** **Which desert reptile warns anyone approaching with a rattling sound?**

a. Sidewinder
b. Rattlesnake
c. Black mamba

**8** **Taking into account its body weight, which is the strongest beetle in the world?**

a. Stag beetle
b. Dung beetle
c. Ladybird

**9** **The largest bird on the planet lives in a desert environment. What is it called?**

a. Rhea
b. Ostrich
c. Kiwi

**10** **What is this bird (right)? One of the places it is found is the Atacama Desert in Chile.**

a. Flamingo  b. Scarlet Ibis  c. Cockatoo

**11** **Which lizard, that is covered in small horns, uses these to collect water?**

a. Monitor lizard  b. Gecko  c. Thorny devil

**12** **What is an oryx?**

a. A type of antelope
b. A type of cat
c. A type of raccoon

# ACROSS THE DESERT

**1** **a. The number of humps.**

Arabian camels, which are also known as dromedaries, have only one hump. Like bactrian camels, dromedaries can travel up to 160 km (100 miles) without water.

**2** **b. Cactus.**

These plants have specially adapted to life in harsh, hot climates. Many species of cactus only flower at night.

**3** **c. Lut Desert.**

A temperature of 70.7°C was recorded by Nasa, by satellite, in the Lut Desert, Iran.

**4** **c. 30%.**

Deserts are not always hot ones. The Gobi desert in Asia is an example of a cold desert, as is Antarctica.

**5** **b. Fennec fox.**

A nocturnal animal, the Fennec fox has massive ears that help it to locate its food source and help it to keep cool.

**6** **a. Desert tortoise.**

This tortoise is truly adapted to living in a desert environment. It can burrow into the ground to avoid the heat of the day and can retain water in its bladder rather than losing it through urination.

7 **b. Rattlesnake.**

Unlike most snakes, rattlesnakes give birth to live young. Their rattle is made from layers of shed skin.

8 **b. Dung beetle.**

These live on every continent on Earth, except for Antarctica. They collect dung and extract the remaining moisture and nutrients from it. Pushing a ball of dung around requires a lot of strength. When dung beetles roll their dung, it is the equivalent of a human pulling 6 double-decker buses!

9 **b. Ostrich.**

Despite being flightless, the ostrich is a fast runner and has a sprinting speed of 70 km per hour (43 miles per hour).

10 **a. Flamingo.**

Flamingos get their colour from pigments in the food they consume.

11 **c. Thorny devil.**

Moisture collects on the many horns that cover the thorny devil. This moisture is then drawn along grooves towards the lizard's mouth.

12 **a. A type of antelope.**

The Arabian oryx is also known as the unicorn of the desert. Their white coats help them to keep cool in the hot desert sun.

# PETS

1

**What two colours would you see on a 'tuxedo cat'?**

a. Black and white
b. White and grey
c. Grey and black

2

**When did humans start to domesticate the dog?**

a. 5 to 10,000 years ago
b. 10 to 30,000 years ago
c. 30 to 50,000 years ago

3

**The dog is a domesticated version of what animal?**

a. Hyena
b. Prairie dog
c. Wolf

4

**What is the most popular breed of dog?**

a. Labrador retriever
b. Beagle
c. German shepherd

5

**Why do some dogs bury bones and toys?**

a. Because it is like storing a kill for a later meal
b. Because they do not want anyone to get their special toy
c. Because dogs love dirt

**6**

**How old was the oldest koi carp in captivity?**

a. 168 years old
b. 203 years old
c. 226 years old

**7**

**Other than being tired, why do dogs yawn?**

a. When they are hungry
b. When they are nervous or excited
c. When they are thirsty

**8**

**Canaries can make excellent pets. What is one of their talents?**

a. They can sing
b. They can fly upside down
c. They smell of bananas

**9**

**How many eyelids does a cat have?**

a. Two b. Three c. Four

**10**

**What is a popular type of pet?**

a. Guinea pig
b. Gambia pig
c. Ghana pig

**11**

**What is one way that people try to calm dogs down during a thunderstorm?**

a. Singing to them
b. Dressing them in tight t-shirts
c. Giving them a cup of tea

**12**

**What is catnip?**

a. A herb used to excite cats
b. A herb used to calm cats down
c. A herb used to help cats sleep

# PETS

**1**

**a. Black and white.**

Tuxedo cats are bicoloured: black and white. Cats are carnivores and even as pets will hunt prey.

**2**

**b. 10 to 30,000 years ago.**

Details on exactly when ancient humans started to domesticate the dog vary as there is little information about our activities at that time.

**3**

**c. Wolf.**

Scientists believe that dogs are descended from a species of wolf that is now extinct.

**4**

**a. Labrador retriever.**

These loyal, friendly dogs get their name from Labrador—a cold northern area of Canada.

**5**

**a. Because it is like storing a kill for a later meal.**

Dogs still retain some aspects of their wolf ancestry: they sometimes bury bones or toys, as a wolf might bury one of its kills to return to later.

**6**

**c. 226 years old.**

These freshwater fish come from eastern Asia.

**7**

**b. When they are nervous or excited.**

Dogs also communicate by urinating on things such as fenceposts, leaving their scent there for other dogs to smell.

**8**

**a. They can sing.**

Male canaries are so good at singing, they can switch quickly between different melodies.

**9**

**b. Three.**

Cats have a lower and upper eyelid and also a third, called a nictitating membrane, that helps to keep the eye clean.

**10**

**a. Guinea pig.**

Guinea pigs aren't pigs and they aren't from Guinea. They were introduced to Europe by the returning Spanish Conquistadors and were a popular pet in Elizabethan times.

**11**

**b. Dressing them in tight t-shirts.**

Dogs can get very nervous when there is thunder and lightning. One method of keeping them calm is to dress them in tight clothing. The feeling of the clothing helps to comfort the frightened dog.

**12**

**a. A herb used to excite cats.**

Some reactions to catnip include rolling around and flipping over.

# DINOSAURS

TRUE or FALSE

1

Dinosaurs had feathers.

2

Birds are dinosaurs.

3

People who study dinosaurs are called archaeologists.

4

In 1853, the man who gave dinosaurs their name had a dinner party set inside an Iguanodon.

5

In the time of the dinosaurs, a day was 23 hours long, not 24.

6

A meteor strike 65 million years ago killed off the dinosaurs. The rock that hit was the size of San Fransisco.

**DID YOU KNOW?**

There is an asteroid named after the Brachiosaurus in the Solar System's asteroid belt.

**7**

The Brachiosaurus was a carnivorous dinosaur.

**8**

The last major extinction was 65 million years ago.

**9**

Triceratops, a dinosaur that lived in the Cretaceous period (just before the dinosaurs became extinct) has a name that means three-horned face.

**10**

The largest dinosaur was called the Argentinosaurus.

**11**

Pterosaurs were flying reptiles that lived alongside dinosaurs. The smallest of these was similar in size to a sparrow.

**12**

T-Rex's vision was based on movement.

# DINOSAURS

## TRUE or FALSE

**1**

TRUE.
The Velociraptor, made famous by Jurassic Park, had feathers and was about 1m tall and up to 2m in length.

**2**

TRUE.
Birds evolved from Therapods – meat eating dinosaurs – so yes, they are living dinosaurs!

**3**

FALSE.
They are called paleontologists. However, paleontologists study all kinds of fossils from all kinds of organisms to help figure out life's origins on Earth.

**4**

TRUE.
Robert Owen was the scientist and he set up a London dinner party inside a model of a dinosaur.

**5**

TRUE.
The moon is the key as to why a day was shorter when dinosaurs roamed the Earth. The moon acts to slow the rotation of the earth. Back in the time of the dinosaurs, the Earth was spinning faster than it is now.

**6**

**TRUE.**
The asteroid hit the planet near the Yucatan peninsula in modern-day Mexico. When it hit, it sent lots of earth into the air – creating a shroud that lasted for many months.

**7**

**FALSE.**
Despite its huge size (Brachiosauruses could grow to around 13 metres tall and 26 metres long) this dinosaur ate only plants.

**8**

**TRUE.**
There is growing concern that another mass extinction is underway – this one is called the Holocene extinction but is sometimes called the Anthropocene extinction in recognition of the role humans have played in destroying habitats and making species go extinct.

**9**

**TRUE.**
Despite their scary appearance, Triceratops were herbivores – they only ate plants.

**10**

**TRUE.**
It is believed that the Argentinosaurus could have weighed as much as 16 African elephants.

**11**

**TRUE.**
Pterosaurs came in all sizes. One had a wingspan larger than that of a modern day fighter jet.

**12**

**FALSE.**
These magnificent predators could grow to 6 metres tall and 12 metres long. There is no evidence for the common belief that T-rex's vision was based on movement.

# SCIENCE and TECHNOLOGY

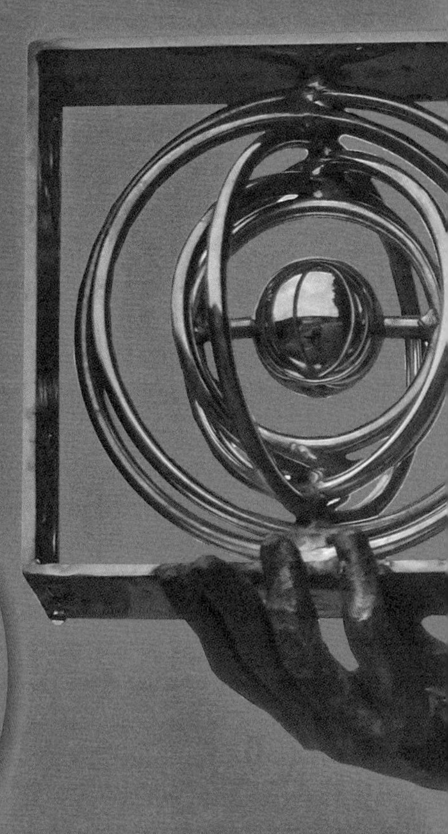

**MARIE CURIE** was the **FIRST WINNER** of **TWO NOBEL PRIZES** and one of only two people to have Nobel Prizes in **TWO FIELDS.**

# CATEGORY 4

# INVENTIONS

### 1

**When was the bicycle invented?**

a. 1717
b. 1817
c. 1917

### 2

**On New Year's Eve, 1879, Thomas Edison lit up the world with which invention?**

a. Light bulb
b. Neon tube
c. Light saber

### 3

**What was the inventor Nikola Tesla most famous for?**

a. His diaries
b. His work with electricity and radio
c. Refusing the Nobel Prize

### 4

**Who invented the dots and dashes code for sending messages?**

a. Samuel Morse
b. Emil Code
c. Francis de Telegraph

### 5

**Edmund Jenner is responsible for saving countless lives thanks to his invention. What was it?**

a. Seat belt
b. Vaccines
c. Parachute

### 6

**When was the vending machine invented?**

a. 1st century AD
b. 10th century AD
c. 20th century AD

### 7

**Bill Gates is famous for working with computers. What did he invent at the age of just 15?**

a. A games console
b. A traffic management system
c. A new kind of telescope

## 8

**When was plastic first invented?**

a. 1862
b. 1916
c. 1949

## 9

**What was the straw first invented for?**

a. Blowing soap bubbles
b. Drinking beer
c. Shooting peas

## 10

**When an inventor invents something, they protect it by registering a document known as a what?**

a. Will
b. Patent
c. Contract

## 11

**What was the name of the Italian inventor, known for his work in electricity/power, physics and chemistry?**

a. Alessandro Volta
b. Leonardo Wirey
c. Vitorrio Amplifier

## 12

**What inspired the invention of the microwave?**

a. Steaming vegetables
b. Melting chocolate
c. Boiling water

## 13

**Which country does the inventor of the paper clip come from?**

a. Sweden
b. Greece
c. USA

## 14

**What invention, used in navigation, is made using a magnet and a needle?**

a. A map
b. A compass
c. A sextant

## 15

**These brothers were not wrong when they invented the world's first aeroplane. What was their name?**

a. The Yeah brothers
b. The Wright brothers
c. The Correct brothers

# INVENTIONS

## 1

**b. 1817.**

A German baron, Karl von Drais, invented a two wheeled device to help him get around. Called a 'draisine', it was the template for what would become the modern bicycle.

## 2

**a. Light bulb.**

While there had been other inventions around the time related to producing electric light, the light bulb that was presented by Thomas Edison is the one that stuck.

## 3

**b. His work with electricity and radio.**

Tesla found out that the performance of electrical machines was optimised when an alternating current was used, meaning the flow of electricity reverses back and forth.

## 4

**a. Samuel Morse.**

Samuel Morse had set out to be a famous painter, but an interest in electro-magnetism led him to develop a telegraph system that used a simple code of his own design.

## 5

**b. Vaccines.**

Vaccines have saved countless lives around the world since their invention in the late 18th century. Edward Jenner developed the vaccine that stopped the spread of smallpox.

## 6

**a. 1st century AD.**

The first vending machine was invented by Hero of Alexandria in the first century. When a coin was dropped into a slot, its weight would pull a cork out of a spigot and the machine would dispense a trickle of holy water.

## 7

**b. A traffic management system.**

Bill Gates invented a traffic control system for the American city of Seattle when he was only 15 years old! From an early age, he says he's been interested in solving problems. Currently, his foundation is working to eradicate polio around the world.

## 8

**a. 1862.**

Plastic was first created by Alexander Parkes, who publicly showcased it at the Great International Exhibition in London in 1862.

## 9

**b. Drinking beer.**

Sumerian brewers are probably the first to invent the drinking straw. They needed to taste the beer at different stages during the brewing process, without removing the fermenting ingredients that floated on the top of the container.

## 10

**b. Patent.**

A patent is something inventors apply for to make sure no one makes, uses or sells their invention without permission.

## 11

**a. Allesandro Volta.**

When you next see 'Volts' on an electrical appliance, think about the Italian inventor who helped to make the modern world what it is.

## 12

**b. Melting chocolate.**

Not all inventions are made on purpose. One day, while working on a machine named a magnetron, an engineer named Percy Spencer noticed that the chocolate bar he had in his pocket for later had melted. Years later he brought out the first microwave oven.

## 13

**c. USA.**

The first paper clip was patented in US by Samuel B. Fay. The shape we know today was the Gem paper clip developed by the Gem Office Products Company but never patented.

## 14

**b. A compass.**

Compasses use magnetised needles that line up with the Earth's own magnetic field.

## 15

**b. The Wright brothers.**

In 1903, at Kill Devil Hills in North Carolina, USA, Wilbur and Orville Wright became the first people to fly. The longest flight they managed that day lasted less than a minute and the plane travelled 260 m (852 feet).

# THE ELEMENTS

**1**

**What is an element?**

a. A metal
b. A chemical that is made of one type of atom
c. A single atom

**2**

**What is the most common element found in the universe? (It also happens to be the lightest element.)**

a. Hydrogen b. Oxygen
c. Carbon

**3**

**In ancient times, 'the elements' meant something different than it does today. What was it?**

a. Gold, silver, diamonds and rubies
b. Head, shoulders, knees and toes
c. Earth, air, wind and fire

**4**

**What is the periodic table?**

a. A table that has a calendar built into it
b. A system of organising the elements
c. A piece of lab equipment

**5**

**How many elements are required to manufacture one standard smartphone?**

a. 30 b. 50 c. 75

**6**

**What is the centre of an atom called?**

a. The core
b. The nucleus
c. The fulcrum

**7**

**How many elements are named after a person?**

a. 2 b. 8 c. 17

**8** **What substance are most of the elements made of?**

a. Wood b. Metal
c. Water

**9** **Which element can be found on Earth as diamonds and as coal?**

a. Carbon b. Sodium
c. Neon

**10** **The atomic symbol for lead is Pb. What does Pb stand for?**

a. Plumbum
b. Polyblue
c. Poobee

**11** **What increases in the presence of helium?**

a. The number of balloons at a party
b. Temperature
c. The speed of sound

**12** **Which of these letters do not appear on the periodic table?**

a. J b. X c. M

**13** **What is the name given to substances that are initially involved in a chemical reaction?**

a. Surfactants
b. Reactants
c. Reagent

**14** **The air we breathe is made up of several different gases, but which one makes up the biggest part?**

a. Oxygen b. Helium
c. Nitrogen

**15** **What is the name of the metal that is liquid at room temperature?**

a. Mercury b. Silver
c. Tin

# THE ELEMENTS

**1**

**b. A chemical that is made of one type of atom.**
An element is a substance that cannot be broken down into other substances.

**2**

**a. Hydrogen.**
Hydrogen is the simplest element. It is also the lightest. Scientists estimate that hydrogen accounts for about three-quarters of the mass of the whole universe.

**3**

**c. Earth, air, wind and fire.**
Ancient Greeks believed the universe was made up of four elements. This viewpoint remained virtually unchanged for over 2,000 years!

**4**

**b. A system of organising the elements.**
The table oraganises the elements by their atomic weight.

**5**

**c. 75.**
Many elements used in mobile phones (smart phones) are scarce and some may run out. Despite this many discarded phones are not properly recycled.

**6**

**b. The nucleus.**
Atoms are the smallest building blocks of matter. At the centre of each atom is the nucleus, which contains tiny particles called protons and neutrons.

**7**

**c. 17.**
Of the 17 elements named after people, only two are named after women: Meitnerium, named after Lise Meitner, a physicist; and Curium, named after Marie (and her hus[illegible] Pierre) Curie.

**8**

**b. Metal.**
Most of the elements –around 80%–in the periodic table are metals of one kind or another. Some examples that you might recognise inlcude the element labelled Au (gold) and one labelled Pb (lead).

**9**

**a. Carbon.**
As strange as it may seem, coal and diamonds are made of exactly the same element: carbon. The difference is in how the carbon atoms are arranged in these substances.

**10**

**a. Plumbum.**
The word 'lead' in the Latin language is 'Plumbum'. It is also where we get the word 'plumbing' from because the first pipes for plumbing were made out of lead.

**11**

**c. The speed of sound.**
The element helium is much lighter and less dense than air. This means that sound travels faster when in a helium atmosphere. It is also why inhaling helium makes your voice go squeaky.

**12**

**a. J.**
Elements' abbreviations are based on their Latin names. The Latin language does not contain the letter J.

**13**

**b. Reactants.**
Reactants are substances that take part in, and undergo chemical changes during a chemical reaction.

**14**

**c. Nitrogen.**
By volume, dry air contains around 78% nitrogen, 21% oxygen, 1% argon and small amounts of other gases.

**15**

**a. Mercury.**
As mercury is a liquid at room temperature and expands as it gets warmer, it is used in measuring devices such as thermometers (which measure heat).

# HUMAN BODY

**1** **What job does your heart do?**
a. Helps the body to digest food
b. Strengthens the immune system
c. Pumps blood around the body

**2** **Where can you find the smallest bone in the body?**
a. The hand b. The ankle c. The ear

**3** **How many bones are there in an adult's body?**
a. 65 b. 187 c. 206

**4** **Which organ is the heaviest in the human body?**
a. The heart b. The brain c. The skin

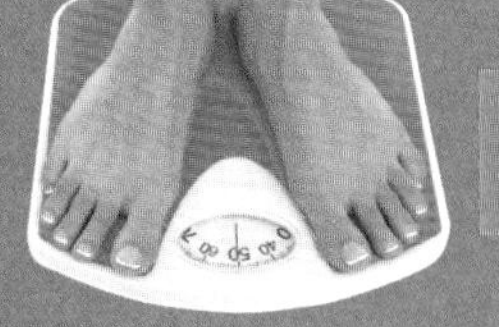

**5** **Which organ helps oxygen enter the body?**
a. The liver b. The kidneys c. The lungs

**6** **Which is the largest muscle?**
a. Upper arm (biceps) b. Jaw (masseter)
c. Buttocks (gluteus maximus)

**7** **Where does our body create new blood cells?**
a. The spleen b. The liver c. The bones

**8** **What are the two holes in your nose called?**
a. Sockets b. Nostrils c. Breath holes

# QUIZ 32

**9** **What are the special structures on your tongue that allow you to taste called?**
a. Taste buds b. Flavour points c. Food sensors

**10** **How much does hair grow on average in one month?**
a. 1.25 cm b. 3.25 cm c. 5.25 cm

**11** **What does your brain send to different parts of your body?**
a. Blood b. Oxygen c. Electrical impulses

**12** **At what stage in life does the body grow the most?**
a. 8–14 years old b. 1–2 years old c. 10–20 years old

**13** **Which type of teeth do we use to effectively chew our food?**
a. Molars b. Canines c. Incisors

**14** **How many chambers does the human heart have?**
a. 6 b. 4 c. 8

**15** **What does the human body use to protect itself when it gets an infection?**
a. The renal system b. The visual system c. The immune system

# HUMAN BODY

**1**

**c. Pumps blood around the body.**
The human heart is the engine of our body, and is responsible for circulating our blood around. It has several different functions, and is a very hard-working organ.

**2**

**c. The ear.**
The smallest bone in the body is in the ear. It is called the stapes and is shaped like a stirrup. It helps you hear.

**3**

**c. 206.**
Babies are born with about 300 bones, but many of these fuse together as you grow. By the time you are an adult, you have 206 bones in your body.

**4**

**c. The skin.**
The skin is the heaviest organ in the human body, and weighs several kilograms.

**5**

**c. The lungs.**
The lungs contain alveoli, which are tiny air sacs surrounded by super small arteries. It is here that oxygen is transferred to the bloodstream.

**6**

**c. Buttocks (gluteus maximus).**
Although the buttocks are the largest muscles in the body, they do not produce the most force.

**7**

**c. The bones.**
Inside your bones, there is a spongy substance called marrow. This is where new blood cells are produced.

**8**

**b. Nostrils.**
Nostrils help you breathe by warming and purifying the air you inhale, and removing moisture when you exhale.

# QUIZ 32 ANSWERS

**9**

**a. Taste buds.**
Your tongue has five main groups of taste buds. These help you taste salty, sweet, bitter, savoury and sour flavours.

**10**

**a. 1.25 cm.**
The average hair growth is 1.25 cm per month, but some people's hair may grow slightly more or less than this.

**11**

**c. Electrical impulses.**
Our brain communicates with nerve cells in the form of electricity. These signals instruct various parts of our body on how to behave.

**12**

**b. 1–2 years old.**
At this stage, our bodies go through the most rapid period of growth in our development. After the age of 2, growth slows down, but does not stop until we are in our mid–late teens!

**13**

**a. Molars.**
These large, flat teeth are at the backs of our mouths. When we chew our food it is these teeth that help grind our food down so we can swallow it safely.

**14**

**b. 4.**
The human heart has four separate chambers. Each one has a separate function in keeping our blood flowing and properly oxygenated.

**15**

**c. The immune system.**
The immune system is our body's defence against illness. Multiple cells and organs work together to keep us healthy. We have different types of special cells that the immune system releases into our bloodstream to attack any intruders.

# PHYSICS

**1**

**What is physics the study of?**

a. Matter, energy and the interaction between them
b. Sports health
c. Cells

**2**

**What is the name of the particle accelerator housed in an enormous laboratory at the French/Swiss border?**

a. Big Bang Machine
b. Large Underground Atomic Experiment
c. Large Hadron Collider

**3**

**Stephen Hawking is best known for explaining the origins of what?**

a. The universe
b. Gravity
c. Extraterrestrial life

**4**

**If you hold the north poles of two magnets together, what happens?**

a. They stick together
b. They push apart
c. They float

**5**

**In physics, a force is defined as a push or a pull on an object. What is force measured in?**

a. Centimetres
b. Newtons
c. Kilograms

**6**

**Which scientist came up with the force of gravity when he observed an apple falling from a tree?**

a. Isaac Newton
b. Albert Einstein
c. Charles Darwin

**7**

**What happens to time at the speed of light?**

a. It speeds up
b. It stops
c. It splits in two

**8**

**When you boil water, the liquid turns into what?**

a. A gas
b. A solid
c. A plasma

Stephen Hawking

**9**

**In a vacuum, if you dropped 1 kg of feathers and 1 kg of lead from the same height, at the same time, what would happen?**

a. The feathers would fall faster than the lead
b. They would fall at the exact same rate
c. The lead would fall faster than the feathers

**10**

**What pattern would you expect to see on an oscilloscope?**

a. Polka dots
b. Waves
c. Tartan

**11**

**Why does a ball fall back to the ground if you throw it, instead of climbing higher and higher?**

a. Because you are not strong enough
b. Because of the force of gravity
c. Because of the force of magnetism

**12**

**The amount of gravity an object has depends on what?**

a. Its colour
b. Its mass
c. Its shape

**13**

**What is the study of optics concerned with?**

a. Microscopes
b. The science of light
c. Optical illusions

**14**

**In the famous equation $E = mc^2$, what does the E stand for?**

a. Electricity
b. Energy
c. Everything

**15**

**The amount of distance an object travels, divided by the time it takes to travel that distance is called what?**

a. Speed
b. Friction
c. Momentum

**DID YOU KNOW?**

**The force of gravity keeps planets in orbit around the Sun.**

# PHYSICS

## 1

**a. Matter, energy and the interaction between them.**

Before it was known as physics, this branch of science was part of what was known as natural philosophy – thinking about how nature works.

## 2

**c. Large Hadron Collider.**

The Large Hadron Collider is a tunnel, shaped in a ring that is 27 km (17 miles) long and is buried beneath the border of France and Switzerland. It accelerates tiny particles and smashes them together to help scientists test theories and solve questions related to physics.

## 3

**a. The universe**

Stephen Hawking was an incredible scientist who worked on the theories of the origin of the universe and black holes. He received many awards for his work including the 1979 Albert Einstein Medal and the 1988 Wolf Prize in Physics.

## 4

**b. They push apart.**

The north pole of a magnet is attracted to the south pole of another magnet and vice versa. When magnets are pushed together, north to north or south to south, they push away from each other.

## 5

**b. Newtons.**

Sir Isaac Newton developed the laws of gravity and motion. His name is used for the units we use to measure force.

## 6

**a. Isaac Newton.**

It makes sense to us that an apple falling from a tree falls to the ground, but Newton thought differently: why, for instance, didn't it fly up into the air, or dash off sideways? His thinking led to his theory of gravity – that all objects are attracted towards each other.

## 7

**b. It stops.**

Einstein's theory of relativity, which has been confirmed by observations, shows that the faster an object travels, the slower time passes for that object.

## 8

**a. A gas.**

Steam is produced when you boil water. Heating things up makes the atoms and molecules in them move more excitedly.

# QUIZ 33 ANSWERS

**9**

**b. They would fall at the exact same rate.**

Even if the objects were not the same mass, they should still fall at the same rate.

**10**

**b. Waves.**

Oscilloscopes are instruments that are used to display the waveform of electrical signals.

**11**

**b. Because of the force of gravity.**

The force of gravity attracts everything that has mass together. That means that although your body is pulled to the surface of the Earth, the Earth is also – ever so slightly – pulled towards you.

**12**

**b. Its mass.**

Mass is different to weight. Weight is the force felt due to the effect of gravity. Mass is a measure of the amount of 'stuff' that is in something.

**13**

**b. The science of light.**

In the 19th century, scientists discovered that the light that we see is only a very small part of a much bigger picture of what light is.

**14**

**b. Energy.**

The equation states that energy is equal to mass (m) multiplied by the square of the speed of light ($c^2$).

**15**

**a. Speed.**

The fastest speed possible is the speed of light, which is 299,792,458 metres per second.

**DID YOU KNOW?**

**The term Physics comes form the Greek word 'physike'. It means 'science of nature'.**

# SCIENTISTS

**1** **Which wild-haired scientist gave us the equation $E = mc^2$?**

a. Albert Einstein  b. Leonard Bernstein  c. Max Planck

**2** **Which scientist invented the alternating current (AC) electric motor, which has formed the basis for the electricity supply system we use today?**

a. Michael Faraday  b. Nikola Tesla
c. Alessandro Volta

**3** **Which famous scientist from Denmark helped map our understanding of the atom?**

a. Guglielmo Marconi  b. Marie Curie  c. Niels Bohr

**4** **Who is the famous Greek philospher (left) associated with a famous theory about triangles?**

a. Plato  b. Pythagoras  c. Pliny

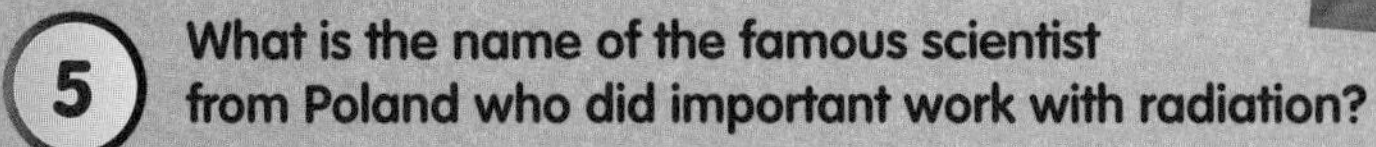

**5** **What is the name of the famous scientist from Poland who did important work with radiation?**

a. Sarah Bernhardt  b. Mata Hari  c. Marie Curie

**6** **Archimedes (below) is a famous scientist from Ancient Greece who famously leapt out of the bath after having a brilliant idea. What word did he shout as he leapt out of the bath?**

a. Eureka!  b. Marvellous!  c. Vulture!

**7** **Which theoretial physicist used to fix radios during The Depression?**

a. Marco Rovelli  b. Richard Feynman
c. Vikram Mukherjee

**8** **Sir Isaac Newton (left) was a mathematician, physicist, astronomer, theologian and author from England. Which branch of mathematics did he invent?**

a. Calculus b. Algebra c. Trigonometry

**9** **Eccentric architect and scientist Buckminster Fuller is most famous for creating the geodesic dome. How many wristwatches was he known wear?**

a. One b. Two c. Three

**10** **Which of these is the title of a book written by Charles Darwin?**

a. The Beginning of Life b. On the Origin of Species
c. The History of Nature

**11** **Which one of these names belongs to one of the most famous primatologists ever?**

a. Jane Goodall b. Emily Blake c. Megan Smith

**12** **Which food hygiene process used with dairy products is named after a French chemist and microbiologist?**

a. Fermentation b. Evaporation c. Pasteurisation

**13** **Galileo Galileo (left) believed in a very controversial model of what?**

a. Our solar system b. The network of nerve cells in the brain
c. The history of nature

**14** **What object has been named after Edwin Hubble, a very well-known astrophycisist?**

a. A microscope b. A magnifying glass c. A telescope

**15** **What did the English scientist Rosalind Franklin do first?**

a. Helped develop the atom bomb
b. Made X-ray images of DNA
c. Designed the Mars Rover

# SCIENTISTS

**1** **a. Albert Einstein.** Albert Einstein (right) is considered one of the greatest geniuses that has ever lived. His simple equation unlocked our ability to understand the universe and how it works.

**2** **b. Nikola Tesla.** Nikola Tesla was born in what is now modern-day Croatia. He is one of the greatest inventors to have ever lived.

**3** **c. Niels Bohr.** Niels Henrik David Bohr was a brilliant physicist. He won the Nobel Prize for Physics in 1922 for his contributions on the structure of an atom, as well as quantum theory. He was also a philosopher.

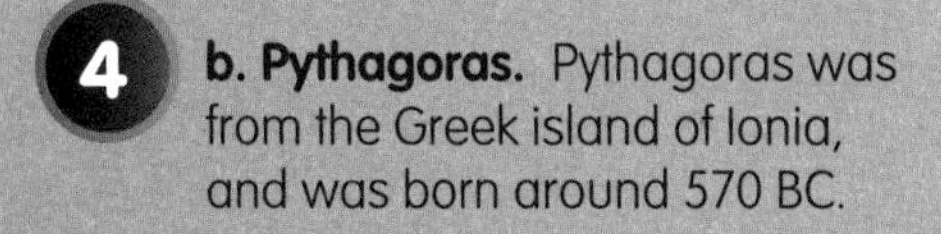

**4** **b. Pythagoras.** Pythagoras was from the Greek island of Ionia, and was born around 570 BC.

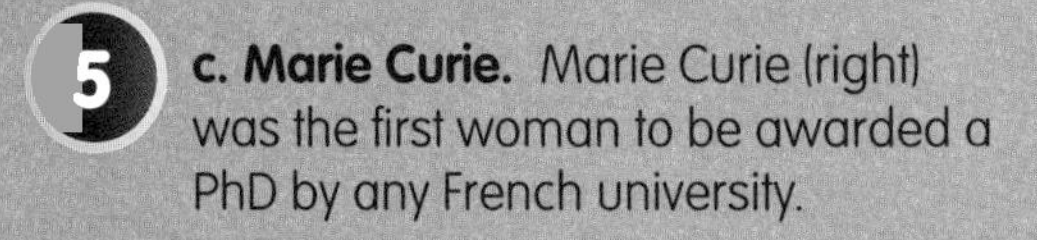

**5** **c. Marie Curie.** Marie Curie (right) was the first woman to be awarded a PhD by any French university.

**6** **a. Eureka!** When he worked out his problem, he was so excited he screamed 'Eureka!' which means 'I have it! and ran naked through the streets to tell the king.

**7** **b. Richard Feynman.** Richard Feynman (left) was a physicist who studied at MIT and Princeton in the USA. He is widely regarded as one of the best theoretical physicists that have ever lived.

**8** **a. Calculus.** When Newton was 22 he was sent home from university to avoid getting bubonic plague. It was during this time that he invented calculus!

**9** **c. Three.** Buckminster wore three wristwatches because he travelled so much. He always wanted to know the time where he was, in the place he was going next and in the place he had left previously.

**10** **b. On the Origin of Species.** Charles Darwin came up with the theory of evolution by natural selection, which shows how species change over time, and how new species come into being.

**11** **a. Jane Goodall.** Born in England in 1934, Jane Goodall (right) studied chimpanzees in their natural environment in great detail. She was named the United Nations Messenger of Peace in 2002.

**12** **c. Pasteurisation.** Louis Pasteur discovered the benefits of heating milk to eliminate germs. He saved countless lives through his work on diseases and the development of immunology.

**13** **a. Our solar system.** Galileo put the Sun at the centre of our solar system, and he was correct. These facts contradicted the powerful Catholic church, and Galileo spent the last years of his life under house arrest.

**14** **c. A telescope.** Edwin Hubble greatly increased our understanding of the size of the universe and was honoured by NASA, who named the powerful Hubble Space Telescope (left) after him.

**15** **b. Made X-ray images of DNA.** Rosalind Franklin took x-ray images of DNA, which enabled the study of the structure of DNA.

# CHEMICAL REACTIONS

**1**

**Where do chemical reactions occur?**

a. In air
b. In water
c. In atoms

**2**

**Most cars rely on a certain chemical reaction to power them. Which of the following is it?**

a. Acidification
b. Evaporation
c. Combustion

**3**

**When one chemical reaction causes other chemical reactions to take place, what is it called?**

a. A chain reaction
b. A crowd reaction
c. A group reaction

**4**

**Your body has billions upon billions of atoms. How old are they?**

a. 100,000 years old
b. 13.8 billion years old
c. 12 trillion years old

**5**

**What is the rarest element?**

a. Astatine b. Barium
c. Tungsten

**6**

**What is steam?**

a. Condensation
b. Mist
c. The gaseous form of water

**7**

**What did the famous Russian chemist Dmitri Mendeleev invent?**

a. The Klein bottle
b. The periodic table
c. The test tube

**8**

**What does the German chemist Robert Bunsen have named after him?**

a. A chemical
b. A theory
c. A burner

**9**

**What is $H_2O$ more commonly known as?**

a. Water b. Soil c. Sand

**10**

**Quantum chemistry is the study of the relationships between the smallest particles in an atom. Who invented this important branch of science?**

a. Albert Einstein
b. Leonardo Da Vinci
c. Erwin Shrödinger

**11**

**Alfred Nobel (most often associated with the prize) was a very talented chemist and inventor. Which of these is he famous for inventing?**

a. Guns b. Dynamite
c. Cannons

**12**

**What is DNA?**

a. A long molecule
b. A type of cell
c. A type of chemical

**13**

**What is the cause of the distinctive smell in the air before a rainstorm?**

a. Acetone
b. Ozone
c. Oxygen

**14**

**What is the only element that won't solidify?**

a. Oxygen b. Carbon
c. Helium

**15**

**How many grams of table salt (NaCl) are in the body of an average adult human?**

a. 250 grams
b. 100 grams
c. 50 grams

# CHEMICAL REACTIONS

**1**

**c. In atoms.**

Chemical reactions occur when chemical bonds between atoms are formed or broken.

**2**

**c. Combustion.**

Burning fuel in a vehicle engine is a chemical reaction that is normally referred to as combustion.

**3**

**a. A chain reaction.**

A chain reaction is when one chemical sets another in action, and this continues on its own. It can be started in different ways, such as light, or an electric spark.

**5**

**a. Astatine.**

Astatine is a radioactive chemical element, and is the rarest naturally occurring element in the Earth's crust.

**6**

**c. The gaseous form of water.**

When water is heated, its atoms begin to move faster and faster, until it eventually causes the water to boil. Once water is at boiling temperature, it produces steam.

**7**

**b. The periodic table.**

Dmitri Ivanovich Mendeleev published the first draft of his periodic table a century and a half ago.

**4**

**b. 13.8 billion years old.**

Although the cells within our bodies are constantly being replaced with new ones, the atoms that make up our bodies have been around since the Big Bang, 13.8 billion years ago!

**8**

**c. A burner.**

Bunsen burners can reach temperatures of 1,500°C (2,700°F).

**9**

**a. Water.**

Water is made up of two hydrogen molecules and one oxygen molecule. This is why chemists refer to it as $H_2O$.

**10**

**c. Erwin Shrödinger.**

Erwin Schrödinger was a Nobel Prize-winning Austrian-Irish physicist and the author of the famous Shrödinger's Cat thought experiment.

**11**

**b. Dynamite.**

Alfred Nobel may not have wanted to be remembered for inventing something that caused death. No one knows for sure, but, he decided that 94% of his total wealth was to be used to award prizes in five areas of human activity (physics, chemistry, medicine, literature and peace-making).

**12**

**a. A long molecule.**

DNA or deoxyribonucleic acid is two long molecules arranged in a spiral that contain all the information needed for an organism to grow and function.

**13**

**b. Ozone.**

Ozone is a a type of oxygen; its name is derived from the Greek word ozein (to smell) because of its sharp, fresh scent.

**14**

**c. Helium.**

Helium is one of the seven noble gases. They are called 'noble' because they are not chemically reactive.

**15**

**a. 250 grams.**

Most of the sodium is in our blood and fluid surrounding our cells. It is lost in sweat and urine.

# TREES AND PLANTS

## 1

**What is the oldest living species of tree currently on Earth?**

a. Bristlecone pine
b. Scots pine
c. Nordman fir

## 2

**What do we call the seed pods that conifers (trees with needles instead of leaves) produce?**

a. Forest fruits
b. Pine cones
c. Spine nuts

## 3

**How many species of plants are known to science?**

a. 55,000
b. 391,000
c. 112,000

## 4

**What do you call the family of plants that trap small insects and eat them?**

a. Insidious plants
b. Ravenous plants
c. Carnivorous plants

## 5

**What is the fastest growing plant?**

a. Bamboo
b. Roses
c. Ivy

## 6

**Why do flowers have pollen?**

a. To feed bees
b. To reproduce
c. To give people hay fever

## 7

**Why do some trees lose their leaves as it gets closer to winter?**

a. To expose more branches to the light
b. Because the tree is getting ready to hibernate
c. Because the tree is dead

## 8

**Why do nettles sting your skin if you brush against them?**

a. Because nettles hate humans
b. As a defence, so they are not eaten
c. Because the leaves are sharp

## 9

**Which of the following is an odd fact about trees?**

a. There is a tree that gets mail
b. There is a tree that grows with its leaves in the ground and its roots in the air
c. There is a tree that can talk

## 10

**What colour did carrots used to be, before we figured out how to change it?**

a. Purple
b. Green
c. Black

## 11

**Whice type of plant is best-known for growing in paddy fields?**

a. Oats
b. Wheat
c. Rice

## 12

**How do plants obtain the energy they need to live?**

a. Respiration
b. Photosynthesis
c. Exhalation

## 13

**Why did cactuses develop protective spines?**

a. For protection
b. To pollinate other cactuses
c. To look interesting

## 14

**What is the tallest species of tree on Earth?**

a. Willow tree
b. Maple tree
c. Sequoia tree

## 15

**How much of the oxygen in the atmosphere do all the plants on our planet make?**

a. 20%
b. 40%
c. 70%

# TREES AND PLANTS

## 1

**a. Bristlecone pine.**

The world's oldest living individual tree is in the USA and is over 5,000 years old.

## 2

**b. Pine cones.**

Pine cones are technically an organ, containing reproductive material even if they don't look like it. The woody cones are female and produce the pine nuts, and the male cones, which are much smaller and harder to spot, produce pollen.

## 3

**b.391,000.**

Recently, scientists assessed the state of all vascular plants in the world, and conclude that there are 391,000 of them. Approximately 369,000 (94%) are flowering.

## 4

**c. Carnivorous plants.**

The Venus flytrap is a plant that captures and digests flies and insects. Other carnivorous plants include the pitcher plant and the sundew.

## 5

**a. Bamboo.**

Bamboo has been observed to grow nearly a metre (91 cm) in a single day!

## 6

**b. To reproduce.**

Pollen is a structure which contains a plant's male DNA. Pollination happens when this is transported to the female part of the flower. Without pollination, plants would not produce seeds or fruit.

## 7

**b. Because the tree is getting ready to hibernate.**

Trees that shed their leaves in the autumn are called deciduous trees. Those that don't are called evergreens.

# QUIZ 36 ANSWERS

## 8

**b. As a defence, so they are not eaten.**

To avoid being eaten by animals, nettles developed stinging cells with hairs filled with acid.

## 9

**a. There is a tree that gets mail.**

This tree is in Germany. It is called 'The Bridegroom Oak' and people who want to find love write letters to it.

## 10

**a. Purple.**

There is a theory that carrots are orange because Dutch growers bred orange varieties to honour William of Orange, who had fought for Dutch independence.

## 11

**c. Rice.**

Despite being associated with Asia, rice is grown on every continent except Antarctica.

## 12

**b. Photosynthesis.**

Plants have cells that convert sunlight into carbohydrates, which can be used as energy. This process is called photosynthesis.

## 13

**a. For protection.**

Many desert cacti have a high perentage of water in their mass, which is tempting to thirsty creatures in a desert environment. They evolved sharp spines to prevent themselves from getting eaten.

## 14

**c. Sequoia tree.**

The tallest specimen currently alive measures over 100 metres! They can be found in California, where they are protected in large national parks.

## 15

**c. 70%.**

An enormous amount of our oxygen comes from marine plants, and plant-like organisms in our oceans and seas.

# MEDICINE

**1** **How long have we had antibiotics for?**

a. Almost 100 years
b. Almost 200 years
c. Almost 300 years

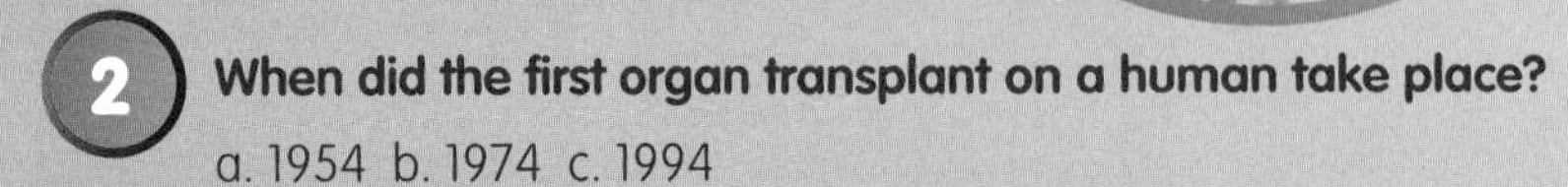

**2** **When did the first organ transplant on a human take place?**

a. 1954 b. 1974 c. 1994

**3** **Who helped discover that insulin can successfully treat the symptoms of diabetes?**

a. Dr Darling b. Dr Banting c. Dr Pepper

**4** **Who was Florence Nightingale?**

a. An opera singer b. A dancer c. A nurse

**5** **What is an epidemic?**

a. An outbreak of disease
b. A type of cell
c. An organ

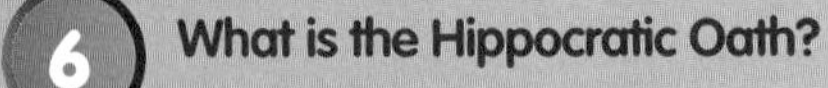

**6** **What is the Hippocratic Oath?**

a. A poem
b. A song
c. A type of promise

**7** **How far back can doctors be traced?**

a. Tens of years ago
b. Thousands of years ago
c. Hundreds of years ago

**8** **Where does the word 'doctor' come from?**

a. Latin b. Russian c. Greek

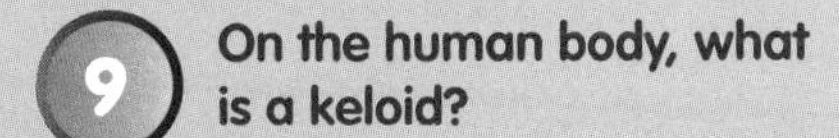

**9** **On the human body, what is a keloid?**

a. A scar b. A rash c. A blister

**10** **Where do many important ingredients for medical drugs come from?**

a. Space b. Plants c. Underground

**11** **What is the surgically implanted device used to help profoundly deaf people to hear called?**

a. A stimulator b. A pacemaker c. A cochlear implant

**12** **Which country was the first to have a birth control clinic?**

a. The UK b. The Netherlands c. Spain

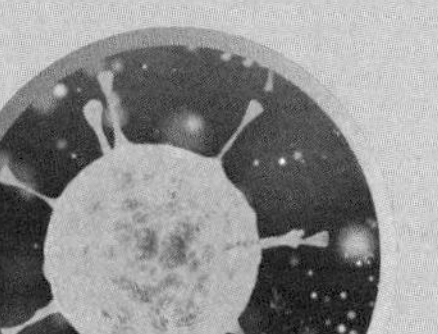

**13** **If you are protected from a disease, what are you said to be?**

a. Inhumane b. Immoral c. Immune

**14** **What is the doctor checking when they tap the patient's knee with a small rubber hammer?**

a. Your skeleton b. Your reflexes c. Your muscles

**15** **What type of surgeon deals with the brain?**

a. A neurosurgeon
b. A cardiac surgeon
c. A plastic surgeon

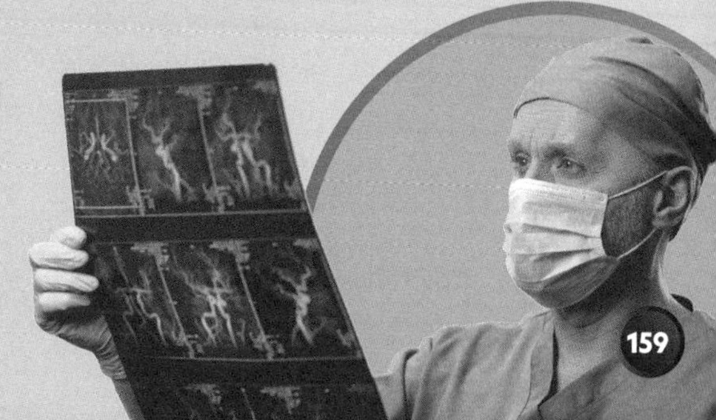

# MEDICINE

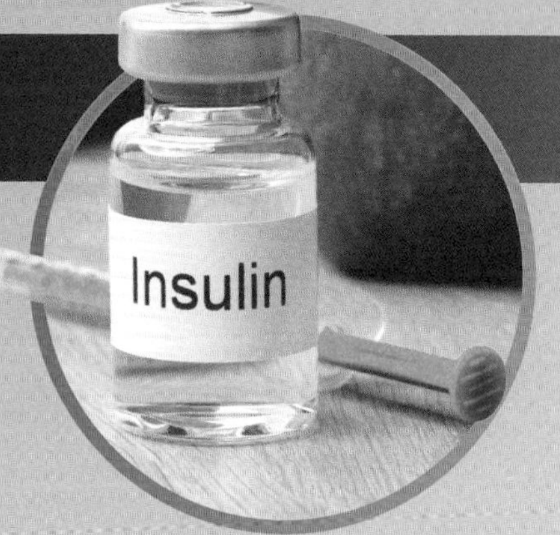


1. **a. Almost 100 years.**

   Penicillin (a type of antibiotic found in mould) was first discovered in 1928, by Alexander Fleming in London, England.

2. **a. 1954.** The kidney was the first human organ to be transplanted successfully.

3. **b. Dr Banting.** Dr Frederick Banting had been studying an organ called the pancreas. This is where our body naturally produces insulin if everything is working as it should.

4. **c. A nurse.** Florence Nightingale was a nurse who wanted to help during the Crimean War. She is widely acknowledged to have changed nursing forever.

5. **a. An outbreak of disease.** An epidemic occurs when an infectious disease spreads rapidly across a wide distance, causing many people to become unwell at the same time.

6. **c. A type of promise.** When doctors are finished with their studies and ready to treat patients, they take the Hippocratic Oath. It was written in Ancient Greece by Hippocrates.

7. **b. Thousands of years ago.**

   We have had doctors since Ancient times. There is evidence of a written prescription from over 4,000 years ago.

**8** **a. Latin.** The term 'doctor' comes from the Latin language (which is not widely spoken anymore). Many English words have Latin roots.

**9** **a. A scar.** Keloids are often raised and uneven, which is different to scars that are flat and smooth.

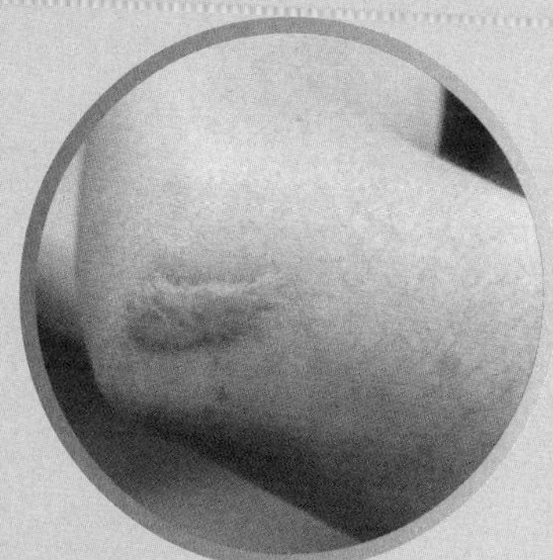

**10** **b. Plants.** Many medicines use ingredients from plants such as morphine (poppies) and asprin (willows).

**11** **c. A cochlear implant.** A cochlear implant is a small device that is implanted by surgeons, which can help people hear. They work by directly stimulating the auditory nerve in the brain.

**12** **b. The Netherlands.** The first clinic was set up in Amsterdam in 1882 by Dr Aletta Jacobs.

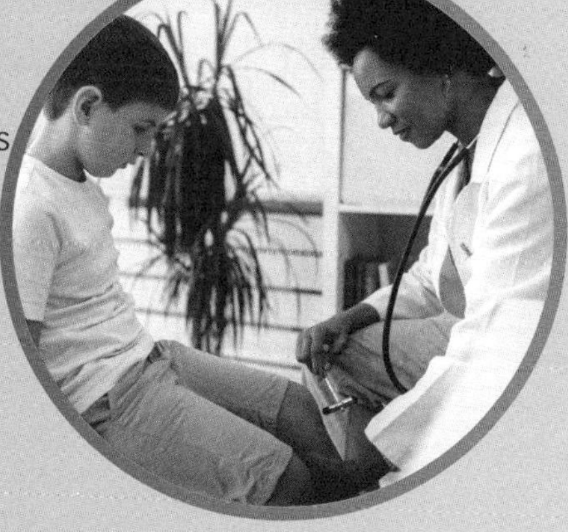

**13** **c. Immune.** If you are immune to a particular disease, then your body has biological defenses to ward it off.

**14** **b. Your reflexes.** The jumping motion is caused by one of our tendons stretching, pulling our quadricep muscle forward.

**15** **a. A neurosurgeon.** A neurosurgeon is a type of doctor who is specially trained to operate on the human nervous system. They often operate on the neck and spine as well.

# COMPUTERS AND THE INTERNET

**1** **Which of these is a computer programming language?**

a. Snek b. Python
c. Baboon

**2** **Lara Croft is the main character in which famous video game series?**

a. Just Cause
b. Tomb Raider
c. Uncharted

**3** **Which of these games was among those released on the first Nintendo Entertainment System?**

a. Duck Hunt
b. Operation Wolf
c. Chase H.Q.

**4** **What do you call a program that you download onto a smartphone**

a. Browser
b. App
c. Motherboard

**5** **What is the name of this early computer-linking or networking system?**

a. ARPANET
b. BARFANET
c. CASTANET

**6** **1 January 2000 was a big day for computers across the world. Why?**

a. It celebrated 100 years of computing
b. People thought that their computers would break
c. The first smartphone went on sale

**7** **A computer bug is a problem in a program that stops it from working. When was the first computer bug found?**

a. 1947 b. 1987 c. 2007

8
**Which of these file sizes is the biggest?**
a. 1 Megabyte
b. 1 Kilobyte c. 1 Gigabyte

9
**What item, named after a furry critter, can you use to move the cursor on a computer screen?**
a. Shrew b. Mouse
c. Vole

10
**Who was the founder of Microsoft, the company responsible for the Windows operating system, and applications such as Word and PowerPoint?**
a. Bill Gates
b. Thomas Edison
c. Steve Jobs

11
**The first webcam was invented to do what?**
a. Check that a pot of coffee was full
b. Spy on an army general
c. Take a selfie

12
**What was the name of the first ever web browser?**
a. Chrome
b. WorldWideWeb
c. Firefox

13
**What was an early name for the system we now know as Windows?**
a. Doors
b. Interface Manager
c. Error 404

14
**What does VR stand for?**
a. Virtual reality
b. Void recognition
c. Visual replay

15
**A computer works using binary. What is binary?**
a. A number system with either a 0 or a 1
b. A type of metal used in circuits
c. A system of wires and plugs

# COMPUTERS AND THE INTERNET

| | |
|---|---|
| 1 | **b. Python.** A programming language allows people to write software and create websites and games. |
| 2 | **b. Tomb Raider.** In the first Tomb Raider game, released in 1996, only six characters are killed. There are plenty of animals (including dinosaurs and gorillas) that meet a sticky end, but only six humans. |
| 3 | **a. Duck Hunt.** The NES launched with 17 titles, including Super Mario Bros. |
| 4 | **b. App.** In 2019, there were over 200 billion app downloads worldwide! |
| 5 | **a. ARPANET.** The internet as we know it wouldn't exist without ARPANET—a system of connecting computers together over long distances—that was developed by the United States government and universities. |
| 6 | **b. People thought that their computers would break.** Because the date was going from 1999 to 2000, many people thought that the computers wouldn't know how to cope with the zeros in 2000 and would break. It was known as the 'millennium bug'. |
| 7 | **a. 1947.** These days, a computer bug is a glitch in a program. In 1947, a scientist at Harvard University in the US found an actual bug in her computer—a moth had got into the machine and was messing up the electronics inside! |

**8** **c. 1 Gigabyte.** A kilobyte is 1,000 bytes, a megabyte is 1,000 kilobytes, and a gigabyte is 1,000 megabytes.

**9** **b. Mouse.** Early versions of this handy little accessory tracked the mouse's movement by means of a ball inside the device, that rolled around. The computer measured the movement of the ball and linked it to the icon on screen.

**10** **a. Bill Gates.** The success of Microsoft's Windows is staggering. Bill Gates and his wife, Melinda, are now using the money they made to improve global health and education.

**11** **a. Check that a pot of coffee was full.** Scientists at Cambridge University in the UK got fed up walking to their coffee room only to find that all the coffee was gone. So they invented the webcam so they could check it without getting up from their desks!

**12** **b. WorldWideWeb.** Tim Berners-Lee, the man who invented the world wide web, made the first web browser.

**13** **b. Interface Manager.** Windows is a GUI—a graphical user interface—the place where the human interacts with the computer.

**14** **a. Virtual reality.** Users put on a headset that projects images into each eye, giving the impression that they are in a 3D computer environment.

**15** **a. A number system with either a 0 or a 1.** Computers store information in bits—a 'bit' is actually short for 'binary digit.'

# Stellar SPACE

You could **JUMP** around **THREE TIMES** higher on **MARS** than you can on **EARTH** beacuse of Mars' **WEAKER** force of **GRAVITY.**

# CATEGORY 5

# SOLAR SYSTEM

**1** **What happened to Ann Hodges as she took a nap on her living room couch in Alabama, USA, in November, 1954?**
a. She missed her nephew landing on the Moon
b. A meteorite smashed through her roof and into her side
c. Aliens abducted her and took her to another galaxy

**2** **Which of the following is a fact about Mercury?**
a. A day on Mercury is twice as long as its year
b. Mercury orbits the Sun in the opposite direction to the other planets
c. Mercury is the coldest planet in the solar system

**3** **If you had a bathtub that was big enough and you filled it with water, what would happen if you put the planet Saturn in it?**
a. It would float  b. It would sink  c. You'd need to call a plumber

**4** **What was the name of the planet that scientists used to think existed between Mercury and the Sun?**
a. Nibiru  b. Vulcan  c. Krypton

**5** **What is the largest planet in the solar system?**
a. Jupiter  b. Saturn  c. Neptune

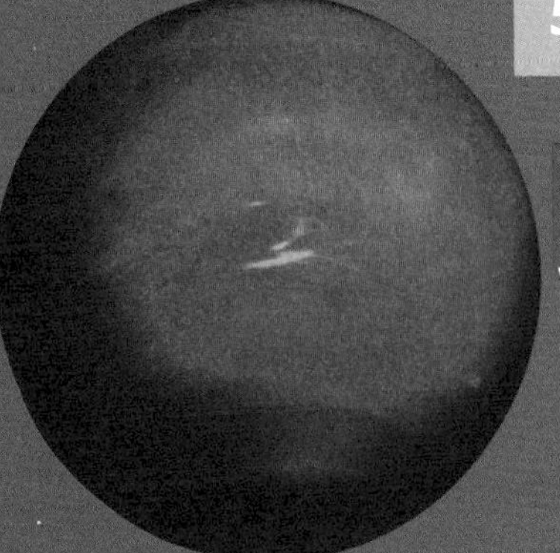

**6** **Which planet, that is about the same size as the Earth, is the hottest planet in the solar system?**
a. Mercury  b. Mars  c. Venus

**7** **Which of these is true of Neptune?**
a. It is the closest planet to the Sun
b. It is the smallest planet
c. It is the furthest planet from the Sun

# QUIZ 39

**8** **One of the planets spins on its side. Which one?**
a. Mercury b. Jupiter c. Uranus

**9** **There is a storm on Jupiter called the 'Great Red ...'?**
a. Dot b. Spot c. Hole

**10** **Saturn's rings are one of the wonders of the solar system. Approximately, how wide are they?**
a. 2,800 kilometres b. 28,000 kilometres c. 280,000 kilometres

**11** **The asteroid belt is between which two planets?**
a. Mars and Jupiter b. Earth and Mars c. Jupiter and Saturn

**12** **There is a dwarf planet hidden within the solar system's asteroid belt. What is it called?**
a. Epox b. Ceres c. Pluto

**DID YOU KNOW?**

**A solar system is a group of planets, meteors, or other objects that orbit a large star.**

**13** **When did the solar system form?**
a. 4,500 years ago b. 4.5 million years ago c. 4.5 billion years ago

**14** **Which planet has the most volcanoes?**
a. Venus b. Earth c. Mars

**15** **Which planet is the only one in the solar system to have water in its solid, liquid and gaseous states?**
a. Venus b. Jupiter c. Earth

# SOLAR SYSTEM

**1**

**b. A meteorite smashed through her roof and into her side.** Meteors burn up in the Earth's atmosphere. Meteorites are meteors that make it to Earth. They are much rarer than meteors, which makes Ann Hodges an unlucky lady!

**2**

**a. A day on Mercury is twice as long as its year.** Because Mercury is so close to the Sun, it only takes 88 days to complete an orbit. Although it only takes 59 days to rotate on it's axis (one day on Earth) it has to rotate twice to have a complete day and a complete night, 176 days in total, meaning a day on Mercury is twice as long as its year.

**3**

**a. It would float.** Saturn is a gas giant and is less dense than water, so if you could put the planet into a bath, it would float (although the rings would probably get soggy)!

**4**

**b. Vulcan.** Mercury has an odd orbit, which scientists had explained by the presence of another, unseen planet.

**5**

**a. Jupiter.** Jupiter is over 300 times as big as the Earth and is the fourth brightest object in the night sky (after the Sun, the Moon and Venus).

**6**

**c. Venus.** With an average temperature of 462°C, Venus is the hottest planet in the solar system. The heat is caused by a greenhouse effect: Venus has thick clouds that trap the heat from the Sun.

**7**

**c. It is the furthest planet from the Sun.** From its discovery in 1930 to the end of the 20th century, Pluto was considered to be the ninth planet, but was demoted to a dwarf planet as its gravitational effect is not strong enough to remove other objects that are close to it.

# QUIZ 39 ANSWERS

**8** **c. Uranus.** Some scientists think that an object as large as a planet smashed into Uranus early on in its history, which pushed it on its side.

**9** **b. Spot.** The Great Red Spot is a storm, like a hurricane, that is around 16,350 km wide – that's larger than the diameter of Earth!

**DID YOU KNOW?**

**Saturn is the sixth planet from the Sun.**

**10** **c. 280,000 kilometres.** Saturn has many rings – between 500 and 1000 – that are made of ice or ice-covered rocks.

**11** **a. Mars and Jupiter.** Separating the rocky planets of the 'inner' solar system from the gas giants of the 'outer' solar system is a belt of millions of small lumps of rock and ice: these are left over bits from the formation of the solar system.

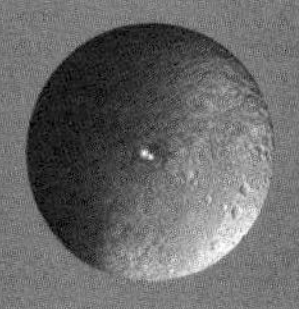

**12** **b. Ceres.** Ceres is the smallest of the dwarf planets. It is only 950 km (590 miles) in diameter.

**13** **c. 4.5 billion years ago.** Scientists have dated meteorites as being 4.6 billion years old. Meteorites are remnants from the time of the solar system's creation, so their age gives us an accurate age of our solar system.

**14** **a. Venus.** Venus has over 1,600 major volcanoes. One of the planet's mountain ranges, 'Maxwell Montes', is taller than Mount Everest – rising 11 kilometres above the Venusian landscape.

**15** **c. Earth.** Earth is the third planet from the Sun and the only place in the solar system that we know of that supports life.

# MOONS

**1**

**Which Apollo mission was the first to put a human on the Moon?**

a. Apollo 1 b. Apollo 7
c. Apollo 11

**2**

**How many people have walked on the Moon?**

a. 11 b. 12 c. 13

**3**

**Which Apollo mission is famous for the fact that it was almost a tragedy?**

a. Apollo 11 b. Apollo 12
c. Apollo 13

**4**

**In Japan, rather than a 'Man in the Moon', what animal do they see?**

a. Cat b. Dog c. Rabbit

**5**

**What is Pluto's largest moon called?**

a. Charon
b. Hades c. Styx

**6**

**Which planet's moons are named after characters in plays by William Shakespeare?**

a. Jupiter b. Venus
c. Uranus

**7**

**How many moons are there in the solar system?**

a. 58
b. 108
c. 158

**8**

**Which planet in the solar system is the only one to have one moon?**

a. Venus b. Earth
c. Mars

**9** Which moon of Jupiter has a partially frozen ocean?

a. Io b. Europa
c. Callisto

**10** There are large dark patches on the surface of Earth's moon. These are known as what?

a. Martha b. Maria
c. Matty

**11** The Earth's moon is roughly the same size as which other planet in the solar system?

a. Mercury b. Pluto c. Mars

**12** What is the biggest moon in the solar system?

a. The Moon (Earth)
b. Ganymede (Jupiter)
c. Titan (Saturn)

**13** What sports equipment could you find on the Moon?

a. Basketballs
b. Golf balls
c. Bowling balls

**14** Titan, the largest of Saturn's moons, is the only moon in the solar system to have what?

a. Volcanoes
b. Clouds
c. Craters

**15** Which planet's moon has a day that lasts for almost an Earth month, and temperatures that range from –169°C to 117°C?

a. Venus
b. Earth
c. Mars

# MOONS

**1**

**c. Apollo 11.**

In July 1969, Neil Armstrong and Buzz Aldrin became the first humans in history to walk on the lunar surface.

**2**

**b. 12.**

The first man to walk on the Moon was Neil Armstrong, in 1969. The last person to walk on the Moon was Gene Cernan, in 1972. All of the people to have walked on the Moon are American men.

**3**

**c. Apollo 13.**

En route to the Moon, there was a catastrophic explosion that left the crew of three traveling away from Earth with limited power, heating, food and water.

**4**

**c. Rabbit.**

The effect of seeing a face (or an animal) in an object is called pareidolia.

**5**

**a. Charon.**

In Greek mythology, Charon took the souls of those who had received a proper burial across the rivers Styx and Acheron to the world of the dead.

**6**

**c. Uranus.**

Characters such as Ophelia (Hamlet) and Prospero (The Tempest) have been used to name the moons of Uranus.

**7**

**c. 158.**

NASA has 158 confirmed moons but there are many provisional moons currently being observed.

## QUIZ 40 ANSWERS

**8**

**b. Earth.**

Earth's moon is also the fifth largest moon in the solar system – it is very large considering the size of the Earth.

**9**

**b. Europa.**

Europa also has a thin atmosphere of oxygen. It seems to be the only place in the solar system, other than Earth, that has the ingredients needed to support life.

**10**

**b. Maria.**

They are called 'maria' from Latin 'mer' which is 'sea'. But they are not seas, they are volcanic plains of basalt.

**11**

**a. Mercury.**

Callisto, one of Jupiter's moons, is also about the same size as Mercury.

**12**

**b. Ganymede (Jupiter).**

Unsurprisingly, the largest planet in the solar system is host to the largest natural satellite.

**13**

**b. Golf balls.**

They were left on the Moon by astronaut Alan Shepard, from the Apollo 14 mission in 1971.

**14**

**b. Clouds.**

Titan has an atmosphere with clouds and rain.

**15**

**b. Earth.**

A day on the Moon is almost exactly the same as the amount of time it takes for the Moon to orbit once around the Earth. This is why we only ever see one face of the Moon.

# STARS

**1**

**Polaris is the name of which star, used by navigators for centuries?**

a. The North Star
b. The Dog Star
c. The Lone Star

**2**

**Which one of the following is the place where a star is born?**

a. Black hole
b. Nebula
c. Quasar

**3**

**Which of the following is a type of star?**

a. Proton star
b. Neutron star
c. Electron star

**4**

**What kind of pollution might prevent you from stargazing?**

a. Air pollution
b. Noise pollution
c. Light pollution

**5**

**The brightest star in the night sky is called Sirius. What other name is it known as?**

a. The Cat Star
b. The Dog Star
c. The Mouse Star

**6**

**How many stars are in a binary star system?**

a. Two
b. Three
c. Four

**7**

**What is the name given to the biggest stars in the universe?**

a. Megastars
b. Hypergiants
c. Supernovas

**8**

**How many constellations are there in the night sky?**

a. 66
b. 77
c. 88

**DID YOU KNOW?**

**The constellations you can see change depending on which hemisphere you are in.**

9

**How many constellations are named after dogs?**

a. Three
b. Seven
c. Fifteen

10

**In Ancient Rome, astronomers called the band of light across the night sky 'via lactea'. What do we translate this as?**

a. The Light Path
b. The Milky Way
c. The Star Pavement

11

**What is an asterism?**

a. A star that can be seen in the daytime
b. A small group of stars
c. A star at the centre of the galaxy

12

**Who painted The Starry Night?**

a. Pablo Picasso
b. Vincent van Gogh
c. Pieter Breugel

13

**Which of these is not a star?**

a. The North Star
b. Sirius
c. The Evening Star

14

**What is a collection of billions of stars, solar systems, dust and gas called?**

a. A quasar
b. A galaxy
c. A universe

15

**Tiny stars that appear to blink on and off like lighthouses in space are known as what?**

a. Pulsars
b. Blinkies
c. Coldstars

# STARS

**1**

**a. The North Star.**
The North Star appears to be a fixed point, around which all of the other stars revolve as the night passes. People have used it to get their bearings for centuries.

**2**

**b. Nebula.**
Nebulae, also called star nurseries, are giant clouds of gas. Gravity causes clumps of gas to accumulate, which leads to the birth of stars.

**3**

**b. Neutron star.**
These stars are created at the end of a massive star's life. Following the star going supernova, the core of the star collapses in on itself, becoming a neutron star – a tiny star with a huge mass and density.

**4**

**c. Light pollution.**
Light pollution, from street-lights, traffic, buildings and stadiums, stops the stars from being visible. It can be harder to appreciate the wonder of the cosmos when you can't see the stars at night.

**5**

**b. The Dog Star.**
The Ancient Greek constellation of Canis Major was a dog, whose nose, Sirius, was called The Dog Star.

**6**

**a. Two.**
Over half of the star systems in our galaxy are thought to be binary systems.

**7**

**b. Hypergiants.**
These stars are truly massive – around 1,700 times as wide as our Sun.

**8**

**c. 88.**
The International Astronomical Union officially recognises 88 constellations.

**DID YOU KNOW?**

**The study of stars, planets and any other non-Earthly bodies is called astronomy.**

9

**a. Three.**
These are Canis Major (Big Dog), Canis Minor (Small Dog) and Canes Venatici (Hunting Dogs).

10

**b. The Milky Way.**
If the conditions are right, and there is no light pollution, the stripe of the Milky Way can be seen by the naked eye.

11

**b. A small group of stars.**
A famous example of an asterism is The Plough (or Big Dipper), which is part of the constellation of Ursa Major (Great Bear).

12

**b. Vincent van Gogh.**
Van Gogh was interested in astronomy and remarked in a letter that he had included the Great Bear in his Starry Night painting.

13

**c. The Evening Star.**
As one of the brightest objects in the night sky, Venus is also known as The Evening Star.

14

**b. A galaxy.**
We estimate that there are between 100 and 400 billion stars in the Milky Way galaxy. And our galaxy is one of billions in the known universe.

15

**a. Pulsars.**
A pulsar is actually a neutron star, the remains of a former massive star. They spin incredibly fast and appear to blink as they emit radiation.

# SPACE TRAVEL

NASA

## 1

**The space probe 'Messenger' flew past three planets before NASA made it crash into which planet?**

a. Mercury
b. Venus
c. Earth

## 2

**The mission to investigate Jupiter, the 'Juno' probe, had what toys on board?**

a. Dominoes
b. Lego
c. Transformers

## 3

**Why has NASA built its launch sites, such as Cape Canaveral in Florida, in the south of the country?**

a. Because it's warmer
b. Because it's closer to the equator
c. Because it's cheaper

## 4

**What was the name of the capsule that took astronauts Neil Armstrong and Buzz Aldrin to the surface of the Moon?**

a. Falcon b. Hawk
c. Eagle

## 5

**The first human being in space was from which country?**

a. The USA
b. The USSR
c. China

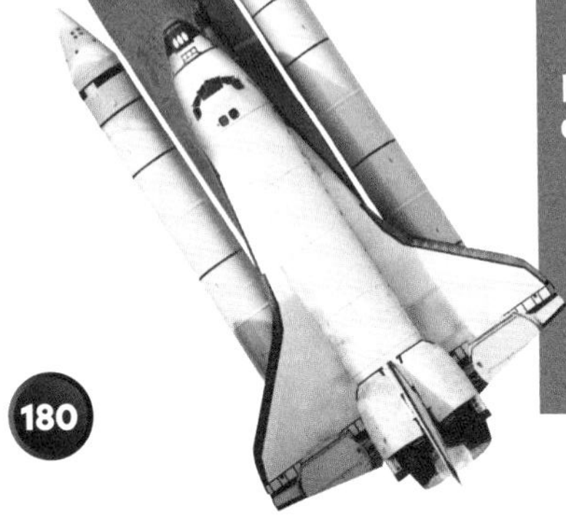

## 6

**In the 1970s, NASA launched two space probes to explore to the edge of the solar system and beyond. What were these probes called?**

a. Starsailor
b. Voyager
c. Enterprise

## 7

**The rocket used to help humans reach the Moon was named after which planet of the solar system?**

a. Jupiter
b. Saturn
c. Venus

# QUIZ 42

## 8

The space shuttle was a reusable spacecraft that was able to transport satellites and other cargo into orbit. How many people could it carry?

a. Three b. Four
c. Eight

## 9

In 2004, the space probe 'Stardust' took samples from the tail of Wild-2. What is Wild-2?

a. A comet
b. An asteroid
c. A dwarf planet

## 10

What was the name of the first ever satellite launched into orbit around the Earth?

a. Thunderbird
b. Sputnik
c. Zvezda

## 11

What is the longest time anyone has been in space for?

a. 238 days
b. 338 days
c. 438 days

## 12

Which country had a space station called 'Mir'?

a. Russia
b. India
c. France

## 13

A new mission to the Moon is named after Apollo's twin sister. What is her name?

a. Merida
b. Freya
c. Artemis

## 14

Launched in 1997, the Cassini-Huygens mission was sent to study one of the solar system's planets and its moons. Which planet did it go to?

a. Saturn b. Jupiter
c. Uranus

## 15

Without the influence of gravity, astronauts actually grow. How much does an astronaut grow, on average in space?

a. 3–4 cm
b. 9–10 cm
c. 15–16 cm

# SPACE TRAVEL

## 1

**a. Mercury.**

The mission was called the MErcury, Science, Space, ENvironment, GEochemistry, Ranging (MESSENGER). It was the first for 30 years that was dedicated to looking at the closest planet to the Sun.

## 2

**b. Lego.**

Small Lego figures—of Galileo and the Roman Gods, Jupiter and Juno —were included as part of the 'crew' on the unmanned mission to the largest planet in the solar system.

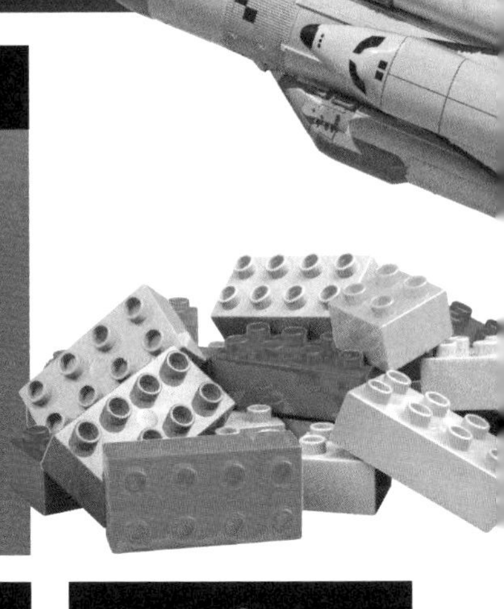

## 3

**b. Because it's closer to the equator.**

Items closer to the equator are moving faster than items closer to the poles. Putting the launch sites at the southernmost positions in the USA gives the rockets a boost as they speed towards outer space.

N

S

## 4

**c. Eagle.**

'The Eagle has landed' were some of the first words spoken from the surface of the Moon.

## 5

**b. The USSR.**

In April 1961, Yuri Gagarin became the first person to be sent into space, orbit the Earth, and return to the surface safely.

## 6

**b. Voyager.**

The Voyager 1 and 2 probes have travelled further than any other human invention. In 2012, Voyager 1 became the first spacecraft to leave the solar system.

## 7

**b. Saturn.**

The Saturn V rocket was the biggest ever built and took all of the Apollo astronauts into low-Earth orbit.

# QUIZ 42 ANSWERS

## 8

**c. Eight.**

The space shuttle program was used to build and refurbish the International Space Station.

## 9

**a. A comet.**

'Stardust' got to within 240 km (149 miles) of the comet and took samples that it brought back to Earth.

## 10

**b. Sputnik.**

The USSR launched the world's first artificial satellite into orbit in October of 1957, triggering a 'Space Race' with the USA.

## 11

**c. 438 days.**

Valeri Polyakov, a Russian cosmonaut, spent well over a year and two months in space on the Russian space station 'Mir' in the 1990s.

## 12

**a. Russia.**

In 1995, the USA's space shuttle docked with Russia's 'Mir,' showing collaboration between the two superpowers.

## 13

**c. Artemis.**

This program will see the first woman on the Moon, and the first man on the Moon since 1972.

## 14

**a. Saturn.**

Launched in 1997, Cassini-Huygens reached Saturn in 2004. After 13 years, Cassini plunged into Saturn's atmosphere.

## 15

**a. 3–4 cm.**

In space, without gravity, astronauts' spines straighten out, meaning they actually grow by a few centimetres. Of course, things go back to normal once they return to Earth.

# DISCOVERIES

TRUE or FALSE

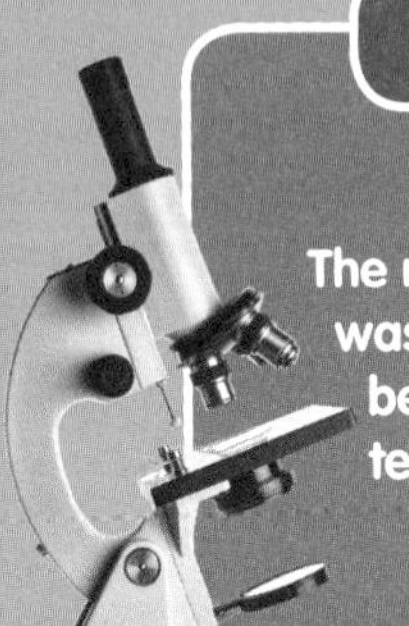

1

The microscope was invented before the telescope.

2

The Sun revolves around the Earth.

3

Sputnik II, the second satellite launched into orbit, had a dog on board.

4

The name of the first space station was 'Skylab'.

5

Radio telescopes are like radio stations for astronomers.

6

The Hubble Space Telescope is the only telescope humans have launched into space.

7

Neil Armstrong's footprints are still on the Moon.

# QUIZ 43

**8**

The first photograph of a star was made in 1850.

**9**

The fastest spinning star ever detected spun at a quarter of the speed of light.

**10**

In 1963, the USSR sent the first woman into space. The USA sent a woman to space for the first time 20 years later.

**11**

An exoplanet is a planet that is outside our solar system.

**12**

Until the 1920s, we did not know there were other galaxies in the universe.

**13**

There is a black hole at the centre of our galaxy.

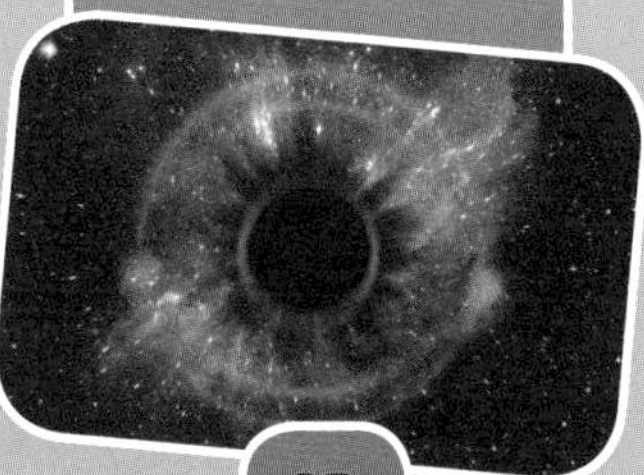

**14**

Pluto was one of the first planets to be discovered.

**15**

The universe is expanding.

# DISCOVERIES

## TRUE or FALSE

**1**

TRUE.
The first microscope was invented around 1590. A patent for the first telescope was made in 1608.

**2**

FALSE.
The Earth, and all of the other planets in the solar system revolve around the Sun.

**3**

TRUE.
The dog's name was Laika. She had been a stray in Moscow, but was picked to be the first animal to orbit the Earth.

**4**

FALSE.
Skylab was the first space station launched by the USA in 1973. The USSR had launched the first space station, Salyut I two years earlier.

**5**

FALSE.
Radio telescopes use radio waves, which are part of the spectrum that includes visible light. Along with the light that we see, stars also give off radio waves that we can collect and understand.

**6**

FALSE.
The Orbiting Astronomical Observatory (OAO-2), launched in 1968, was the first space telescope.

**7**

TRUE.
There is no atmosphere on the Moon, so there is nothing to disturb the footprints.

**8**

TRUE.
William Bond took the first photographic image of a star, named Vega.

**9**

TRUE.
Neutron stars often rotate very quickly, but this star – named PSR J1748–2446ad spun 716 times per second!

**10**

TRUE.
Valentina Tereshkova orbited the Earth in 1963 on board Vostok 6. Sally Ride embarked on mission STS-7 to launch communication satellites in 1983.

**11**

TRUE.
The first exoplanet was discovered in 1992. Since then, over 4,000 planets have been discovered in solar systems other than our own.

**12**

TRUE.
The astronomer Edwin Hubble observed stars within the Andromeda nebula and concluded that Andromeda was actually a galaxy all of its own, containing millions upon millions of stars.

**13**

TRUE.
In fact, the black hole at the centre of the Milky Way is a supermassive black hole.

**DID YOU KNOW?**

Uranus was discovered in 1781 by William Herschel.

**14**

FALSE.
Pluto was discovered in 1930. 75 years later, it was re-classified as a dwarf planet.

**15**

TRUE.
Astronomers have observed that distant galaxies are getting further and further apart from each other. And this is happening all across the observable universe.

# THE SUN

**1**

**What moves in front of the Sun to create a solar eclipse?**

a. The Moon b. Venus
c. A circular cloud

**2**

**Where is the hottest part of the Sun?**

a. The Sun's core
b. The surface of the Sun
c. The atmosphere around the Sun

**3**

**How long does it take light to reach the Earth from the Sun.**

a. 0 seconds b. 8 minutes
c. 8 hours

**4**

**What is a sunspot?**

a. A cooler, darker patch on the Sun
b. A spot you get if you stay out in the Sun for too long
c. A particularly lovely, sunny location on Earth

**5**

**What percentage of hydrogen atoms make up the sun?**

a. 71% b. 81% c. 91%

**6**

**A photon is a particle of light. How long does it take a photon to get from the inside of the Sun to its surface?**

a. 17 seconds b. 170 days
c. 170,000 years

**7**

**How many Earths could fit inside the Sun?**

a. Around 30,000
b. Around 300,000
c. Around 1.3 million

**8**

**Solar flares are bursts of energy from the surface of the Sun. What effect can they cause here on Earth?**

a. Light shows in the sky near the north and south poles (aurora)
b. Thunderstorms
c. Eclipses

**9** How old is the Sun?

a. 146 billion years
b. 4.6 billion years
c. 4.6 million years

**10** How much of the mass of the solar system is made up of the mass of the Sun?

a. About half of it
b. About three-quarters of it
c. Nearly all of it

**11** What symbol do astronomers use for the Sun?

a. ⊙ b. ϕ c. *

**12** What is going to happen to the Sun in 5 billion years?

a. It will shrink and fade
b. It will expand and glow red
c. It will explode

**13** How fast is the Sun travelling?

a. It isn't
b. About 220 kilometres per second
c. At the speed of light

**14** What part of the Sun is visible during a total solar eclipse?

a. The corona
b. The core
c. None of it

**15** What colour is the light given off by the Sun?

a. Yellow b. White
c. Blue

# THE SUN

**1**

**a. The Moon.**
When the Moon passes between the Sun and the Earth, it fully blocks out the disc of the Sun.

**2**

**a. The Sun's core.**
Temperatures can reach 15 million degrees Celcius.

**3**

**b. 8 minutes.**
The Sun is around 150 million kilometres away from the Earth. Even though it travels at 1,080,000,000 kilometres per hour, it still takes 8 minutes for light to reach us from our star.

**4**

**a. A cooler, darker patch on the Sun.**
Sunspots appear because magnetic fields in the Sun stop heat getting to parts of the surface making them cooler and darker.

**5**

**c. 91%.**
Of the remaining 9%, nearly all of it is helium, with other elements making up only 0.1% of the mass of the Sun.

**6**

**c. 170,000 years.**
When released from the Sun, a photon travels at the speed of light. However, it takes a long time for one to be released from the inside of the Sun's furnace.

**7**

**c. Around 1.3 million.**
The Sun is a truly massive object. All objects in the solar system are trapped within the gravity created by the Sun's immense mass.

**8**

**a. Light shows in the sky near the north and south poles.** Solar flares can also disrupt electronic equipment and satellites.

**9**

**b. 4.6 billion years.**
Scientists think that the Sun is about halfway through its life.

**10**

**c. Nearly all of it.**
Over 99% of the mass of the whole solar system is made up of the Sun. The planets, moons, asteroids and everything else make up the rest - less than 1%.

**11**

**a. ☉.**
While there are official names for all kinds of stars (and all of our planets and their moons if they have them) there is no official name for the star closest to us. Astronomers all refer to it as the Sun.

**12**

**b. It will expand and glow red.**
This stage of our Sun's life happens when it has turned all of the hydrogen that it can into helium.

**13**

**b. About 220 kilometres per second.**
It may seem odd to think that the Sun is moving, as the whole solar system revolves around it. But the Sun is orbiting too: it is going around the galaxy.

**14**

**a. The corona.**
The corona is the atmosphere of the Sun. Oddly, the corona is hotter than the surface.

**15**

**b. White.**
The visible part of the energy from the Sun that we see as light is made of all the colours of the rainboW combined.

# THE COSMOS

**1** **Which constellation of stars do we associate with 'The Hunter'?**

a. Orion
b. Leo
c. Aries

**2** **On average, the distance between the centre of the Earth and the centre of the Sun is 150 million km (93 million miles). What is this also known as (it's used as a measure by astronomers)?**

a. Hubble unit b. ES unit c. Astronomical unit

**3** **What do scientists call it when a star explodes?**

a. Greatnova b. Supernova c. Awesomenova

**4** **What is the name of the unknown substance that makes up nearly 30% of our universe?**

a. Hidden space
b. Black holes
c. Dark matter

**5** **When was our universe created?**

a. 13.7 million years ago
b. 13.7 billion years ago
c. 13.7 trillion years ago

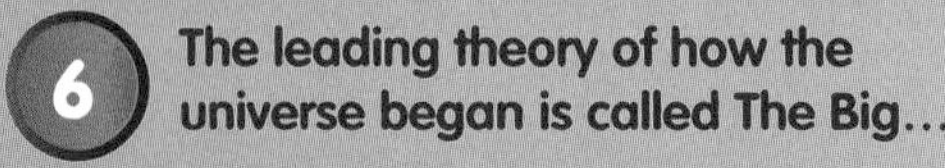

**6** **The leading theory of how the universe began is called The Big…**

a. Boom b. Bang c. Bounce

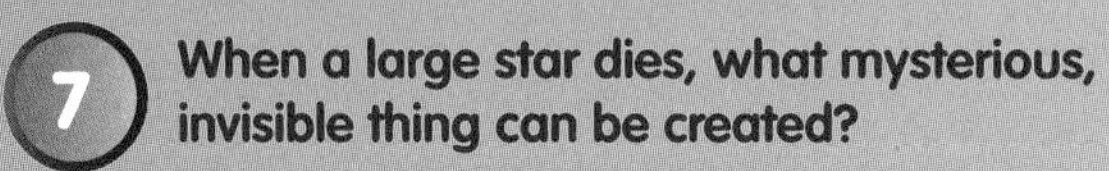

**7** **When a large star dies, what mysterious, invisible thing can be created?**

a. A black hole b. A red dwarf c. A galaxy

**8** **What is the Oort cloud?**

a. A cloud of gas, dust and comets at the edge of the solar system
b. A cloud of gas between Jupiter and Saturn the size of Earth
c. A cloud that has been seen on Neptune for 50 years

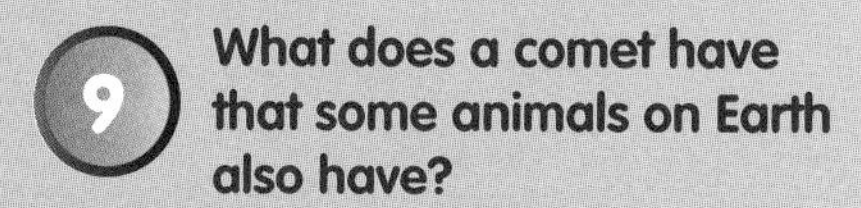

**9** **What does a comet have that some animals on Earth also have?**

a. A tail b. A hoof c. A horn

**10** **What is a light year a measure of?**

a. Time b. Distance c. Speed

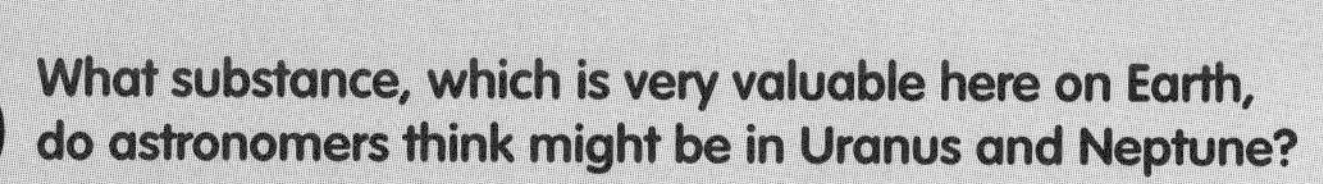

**11** **What substance, which is very valuable here on Earth, do astronomers think might be in Uranus and Neptune?**

a. Liquid gold b. Liquid diamond c. Liquid titanium

**12** **How old is the oldest planet ever discovered?**

a. 4.6 billion years b. 13 billion years c. 100 billion years

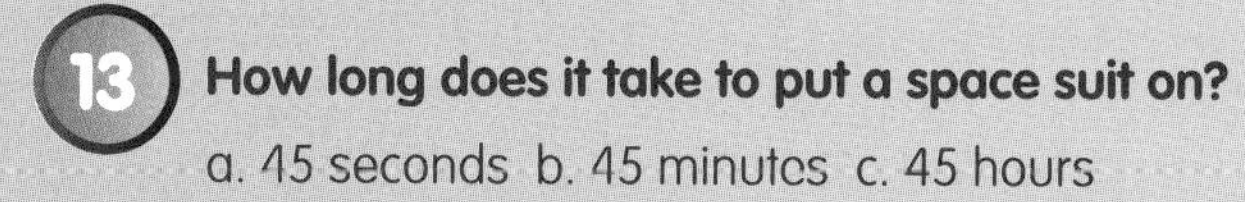

**13** **How long does it take to put a space suit on?**

a. 45 seconds b. 45 minutes c. 45 hours

**14** **The universe is expanding, but this expansion is...**

a. Speeding up b. Slowing down c. Wobbling

**15** **Is there life on other planets?**

a. Yes b. No c. Probably

# THE COSMOS

1. **a. Orion.** The upper-left star in Orion is a star called Betelgeuse. The star's rather odd name comes from Arabic for 'the hand of the central one' which later became 'the hand of Orion'.

2. **c. Astronomical unit.** As well as measuring distances in light years, astronomers also use the Astronomical unit, which is technically 149,597,870.7 km (92,955,807.3 miles).

3. **b. Supernova.** When a star at least five times the size of the Sun runs out of fuel, it collapses in on itself and explodes. When this happens, the explosion outshines its whole galaxy.

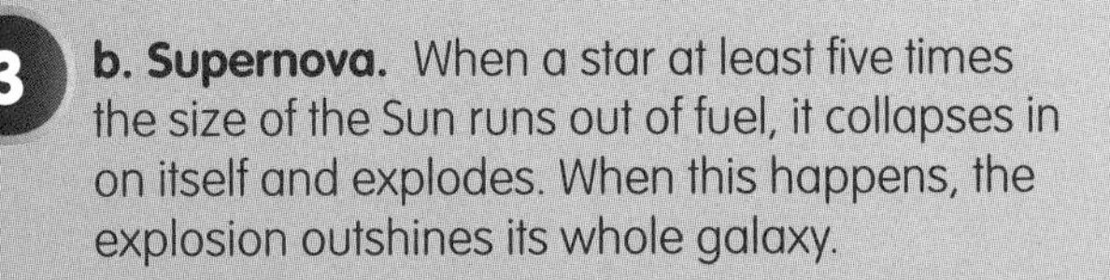

4. **c. Dark matter.** Scientists have calculated that around 68% of the universe is made of energy (called dark energy) and around 27% of the universe is made of matter that we call dark matter.

5. **b. 13.7 billion years ago.** When the universe first started, it was made up of only hot particles, light and energy.

6. **b. Bang.** It is thought that the universe began from a tiny point, which expanded rapidly into the universe we see today.

7. **a. A black hole.** Black holes are impossible to see. Gravity is so strong in a black hole that not even light can escape.

8 **a. A cloud of gas, dust and comets at the edge of the solar system.** This is where the Sun's gravity gets too weak to keep molecules in orbit. It is known as the heliopause, from helio – meaning sun, and pause – meaning stop.

9 **a. A tail.** A comet's tail is made of tiny bits of dust and particles of the comet. However, it doesn't trail behind the comet as you might think – it is actually blown by wind from the Sun!

10 **b. Distance.** A light year is a measure used by scientists and astronauts to describe the vast distances of the universe. It is the distance that a beam of light travels in one year. It is about nine and a half trillion kilometres.

11 **b. Liquid diamond.** When scientists conducted experiments to see if they could liquify a diamond, they succeeded, but got a surprise when they saw solid diamond 'icebergs' that floated in their diamond sea.

12 **b. 13 billion years.** The planet is an exoplanet, meaning it is not in our own solar system. It can be found in the constellation of Scorpius.

13 **b. 45 minutes.** After putting on theit space suit, astronauts then spend over an hour breathing oxygen before leaving the pressure chamber.

14 **a. Speeding up.** Nobody is sure why the expansion of the universe seems to be accelerating. Mysteries like this one are what keep scientists pushing forward to find answers and make new discoveries.

15 **c. Probably.** A project called the Search for Extra-Terrestrial Intelligence is dedicated to looking for signs of life out in the rest of the universe.

# MARS

**1**

**The War of the Worlds is a famous science fiction novel about an aliens from Mars attacking Earth. Who wrote it?**

a. Jules Verne
b. H.G. Wells
c. Dan Brown

**2**

**Why does Mars appear to be red?**

a. Because it is rusty
b. Because it was painted that way by aliens
c. Because it's super hot

**3**

**What was the name of the first spacecraft to land on the surface of Mars?**

a. Mars 1
b. Mars 2
c. Mars 3

**4**

**Olympus Mons is a feature on the Martian surface. What sort of feature is it?**

a. A canyon
b. An extinct volcano
c. An ice cap

**5**

**How long is a year on Mars?**

a. 250 days
b. 365 days
c. 687 days

**6**

**Mars is the _________ planet from the sun?**

a. Second
b. Third
c. Fourth

**7**

**Where does Mars get its name from?**

a. A chocolate bar
b. A Roman god
c. The first king of Ancient Greece

**8**

**How many moons does Mars have?**

a. Two
b. Four
c. Eight

**DID YOU KNOW?**

**A day on Mars lasts for 24 hours and 37 minutes.**

**9**

**What is the name of the longest-running mission to the Martian surface?**

a. Chance
b. Opportunity
c. Luck

**10**

**What did a mission to Mars in 2018 uncover that was quite a surprise to scientists?**

a. There was a colony of Martians living underground
b. There was a lake of water under one of Mars' polar ice caps
c. There was breathable air on Mars

**11**

**What is the diameter of Mars?**

a. 792 kilometres
b. 3,792 kilometres
c. 6,792 kilometres

**12**

**How many spacecraft are currently undertaking missions in Mars' orbit.**

a. One
b. Five
c. Eight

**13**

**How cold can it get on Mars?**

a. – 27°C
b. – 127°C
c. – 227°C

**14**

**Of the planets in our solar system, Mars is the...?**

a. Second hottest
b. Second biggest
c. Second smallest

**15**

**What multicoloured stone, found on Earth and used in jewellery, has also been found on Mars?**

a. Opal
b. Bizmuth
c. Silver

# MARS

**1**

**b. H.G. Wells.**

H.G. Wells also wrote other classic stories of science fiction, including The Invisible Man and The Time Machine.

**2**

**a. Because it is rusty.**

A chemical called iron oxide, which is in the rocks and soil on Mars, gives the planet its famous reddish colour. Iron oxide is commonly known as rust.

**3**

**c. Mars 3.**

Mars 3 lander was a Soviet spacecraft that landed on the Moon in 1971. It stopped transmitting after 20 seconds. No one knows why, but a powerful dust storm may have been the cause.

**4**

**b. An extinct volcano.**

It is the tallest mountain in the solar system. It is about three times the height of Mount Everest!

**5**

**c. 687 days.**

It takes Mars nearly twice as long to orbit the Sun as it does for the Earth.

**6**

**c. Fourth.**

In our solar system, Mars is positioned between Earth and the Asteroid Belt.

**7**

**b. A Roman god.**

The Roman God of War was named Mars. The Romans had copied the Ancient Greeks, who had named the planet after their God of War, who was called Ares.

**8**

**a. Two.**

Mars has two moons, named Phobos and Deimos. They are named after characters in Greek mythology who represented Panic and Dread.

**DID YOU KNOW?**

**In China, Mars is known as the 'Fire Star'.**

9

**b. Opportunity.**

While the mission was only planned for three months, the Opportunity Rover kept going for nearly 15 years!

10

**b. There was a lake of water under one of Mars' polar ice caps.**

Astronomers had long known that there was water on Mars, but thought that it was all stored as ice in the small polar ice-caps.

11

**c. 6,792 kilometres.**

The diameter of Mars is roughly half that of Earth's. The length of a day on Mars is roughly the same as it is here (24 hours).

12

**c. Eight.**

Four more missions are being planned or are on their way and due to arrive in 2021.

13

**b. – 127°C.**

Although temperatures of -127°C have been measured, it is thought it could get as cold as -153°C at Mars' poles. Mars is colder because it has a very thin atmosphere and it is so much further away from the Sun than Earth. Despite this, temperatures can reach up to a pretty pleasant 20°C.

14

**c. Second smallest.**

Mercury is the smallest planet in our solar system, followed by Mars.

15

**a. Opal.**

Bits of Mars have ended up on Earth, in the form of meteorites. One of these revealed that Mars has a type of opal known as a fire opal.

# Spectacular SPORT

Because **TEMPERATURE** affects the bounce of the ball, **TENNIS BALLS** at **WIMBLEDON** are stored at **20°C** (68°F).

# CATEGORY 6

# BATS AND BALLS

**1** **In which sport would you hit a home run?**
a. Baseball b. Basketball c. American football

**2** **How many players are in a basketball team?**
a. Five b. Seven c. Nine

**3** **Which of these is a position in American football?**
a. Nickelback b. Quarterback c. Dimeback

**4** **How do basketball games begin?**
a. Tip off b. Toss up c. Jump start

**5** **The Six Nations is a competition in which sport?**
a. Tennis b. Cricket c. Rugby union

**6** **In golf, which of these is a better score?**
a. Par b. Albatross c. Eagle

**7** **How many players make up a beach volleyball team?**
a. Two b. Four c. Five

**8** **In tennis, which surface is the French Open played on?**
a. Grass b. Rubber c. Clay

**9** **Where was squash invented?**
a. California b. London c. Cardiff

**10** **Polo is usually played with which animal?**
a. Horses b. Dogs c. Fish

# QUIZ 47

**11** **What is a netball court divided into?**
a. Halves b. Thirds c. Quarters

**12** **In lawn bowls, what is the white target ball called?**
a. Snitch b. Jill c. Jack

**13** **Hurling was invented in which country?**
a. Scotland b. Ireland c. Wales

**14** **What are referees in field hockey called?**
a. Umpires b. Officials c. Masters

**15** **How many points is the black ball worth in snooker?**
a. 7 b. 8 c. 9

**16** **What is football sometimes referred to as?**
a. The glorious game b. The wonderful game c. The beautiful game

**17** **What is table tennis also known as?**
a. Mini tennis b. Ping-pong c. Paddle ball

**18** **What is the Test cricket series between England and Australia called?**
a. The Masters b. The Open c. The Ashes

**19** **In goalball, what are embedded into the ball?**
a. Bells b. Sensors c. Weights

**20** **In what decade was the first official beach football tournament?**
a. 1930s b. 1940s c. 1950s

# BATS AND BALLS

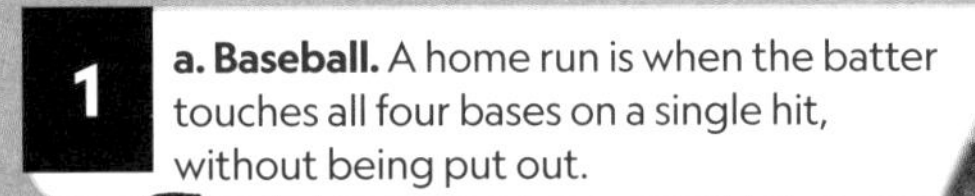

**1** **a. Baseball.** A home run is when the batter touches all four bases on a single hit, without being put out.

**2** **a. Five.** A team is made up of two guards, two forwards an a centre.

**3** **b. Quarterback.** The quarterback's main job is to throw the football and to call the play, so that team-mates know what to do.

**4** **a. Tip off.** This is when the referee tosses the ball between two players from opposing teams, they will then jump to 'tip' or push the ball to their teammates and gain the advantage.

**5** **c. Rugby union.** This is an annual international competition involving the teams: England, France, Ireland, Italy, Scotland and Wales.

**6** **b. Albatross.** Also known as a double eagle, this is the score of three-under-par on a single hole.

**7** **a. Two.** Beach volleyball teams are in pairs but an indoor team has six players.

**8** **c. Clay.** Players can preserve more energy by sliding into shots instead of coming to a complete shop. The bounce of a tennis ball is also higher and slower than that of a harder surface.

**9** **b. London.** In the 1800s, students at Harrow School noticed that a punctured ball squashed on impact with the wall. The first courts were built here.

**10** **a. Horses.** Usually formed of two teams of four players using mallets with long handles. The aim is to drive a wooden ball down a grass field and into a goal.

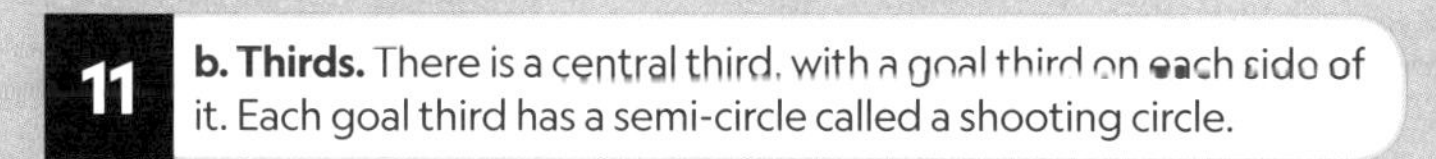

**11** **b. Thirds.** There is a central third, with a goal third on each side of it. Each goal third has a semi-circle called a shooting circle.

**12** **c. Jack.** This precision sport involves players trying to roll their bowl closest to the jack.

**13** **b. Ireland.** Hurling is considered to be the World's oldest and fastest field sport. The fastest shot ever recorded was 181 kmph (112 mph).

**14** **a. Umpires.** This is a person with the authority to make sure players follow the rules of the game.

**15** **a. 7.** With the other balls being worth: red (1), yellow (2), green (3), brown (4), blue (5), pink (6) and black (7).

**16** **c. The beautiful game.** This is a common nickname in mainstream media and advertising, and was popularised by the professional footballer Pelé.

**17** **b. Ping-pong.** Table tennis was invented in England in the early 20th-century. It is a popular sport in China and Japan.

**18** **c. The Ashes.** While the first test match was in Melbourne in 1877, the Ashes legend started after the ninth test match in 1882.

**19** **a. Bells.** Players must use the sound of the bell to judge the position and movement of the ball.

**20** **c. 1950s.** It occurred in Rio de Janeiro, Brazil.

# OLYMPICS

## 1

**Which South American country hosted the 2016 Olympics?**

a. Brazil
b. Argentina
c. Chile

## 2

**How many times has London hosted the Olympic Games?**

a. Three
b. Four
c. Five

## 3

**How many colours make up the Olympic rings?**

a. Three
b. Five
c. Seven

## 4

**How often are the Winter Olympics held?**

a. Every 2 years
b. Every 4 years
c. Every 6 years

## 5

**Where were the first Winter Olympic games held?**

a. Argentina
b. Russia
c. France

## 6

**Which is the only country to have won a gold medal at every Winter Olympic Games?**

a. Sweden
b. Norway
c. USA

## 7

**What year were the first Olympics held?**

a. 1896
b. 1900
c. 1892

## 8

**How many times have the Olympics been cancelled?**

a. Never
b. Twice
c. Three times

## 9

**How many events did the first modern Olympics have?**

a. 3 b. 23 c. 43

## 10

**What are gold medals mostly made of?**

a. Rose gold
b. Silver
c. Bronze

## 11

**How many times has Athens hosted the Olympic Games?**

a. Two
b. Three
c. Four

## 12

**Michael Phelps is the most decorated Olympian. How many medals has he won?**

a. 20
b. 24
c. 28

## 13

**How many events make up the modern pentathlon?**

a. 5
b. 8
c. 7

## 14

**Who is Great Britain's best-known ski jumper?**

a. Sarah the Swift
b. Eddie the Eagle
c. Andy the Albatross

## 15

**Over how many days was the first Summer Olympics staged in London?**

a. 17
b. 56
c. 188

## 16

**Which of these is not an event in the decatholon?**

a. 110 metres hurdles
b. 600 metres sprint
c. Discus throw

## 17

**Where were the equestrian events for the 1956 Melbourne games held?**

a. Stockholm
b. New Zealand
c. Spain

## 18

**Which Olympic Games were the first to be televised?**

a. Berlin b. Barcelona c. Athens

# OLYMPICS

## 1

**a. Brazil.**

It was hosted in Rio de Janeiro from 5–21 August. It was the first time Brazil had held the Olympics.

## 2

**a. Three.**

London held the third Summer Olympic Games in 1908, then again in 1948 and 2012. It is the first city to have hosted the modern Summer Olympic Games three times.

## 3

**b. Five.**

The five rings represent the five continents of the world at the time (1912), united by Olympism. The six colours (white, blue, yellow, black, green and red) represent the colours that appear on all of the national flags of the world.

## 4

**b. Every 4 years.**

It is held every 4 years, like the Summer Olypmics, but it occurs 2 years after.

## 5

**c. France.**

The Games were held in Chamonix, France in 1924.

## 6

**c. USA.**

They have won a gold medal at every Winter Olympics, but Norway leads for the most Winter Olympic medals ever.

## 7

**a. 1896.**

The first was held in Athens, Greece.

## 8

**c. Three times.**

Summer Olympics in 1916 were cancelled due to WWI and both Summer Olympics of 1940 and 1944 were cancelled due to WWII. In 2020, the games were moved back by one year due to the coronavirus.

## 9

**c. 43.**

There are now over 300 events.

## 10

**b. Silver.**

The gold medals haven't been made of solid gold since the 1912 Olympics.

# QUIZ 48 ANSWERS

## 11

**a. Two.**

They held the first ever Olympics in 1896 and then again in 2004.

## 12

**c. 28.**

He is the most decorated Olympian of all time!

## 13

**a. 5.**

These events include: fencing, freestyle, swimming, equestrian show jumping, and a combined event of pistol shooting and cross-country running.

## 14

**b. Eddie the Eagle.**

He competed in the 1988 Olympics, finishing in last place for the 70 m and 90 m events.

## 15

**c. 188.**

That's more than half of the year! The Games' opening ceremony occurred on 13 July 1908, but the Games opened on 27 April with the racquets competition. It ended on 31 October.

## 16

**b. 600 metres sprint.**

The decathlon is a 2-day event filled with track and field events such as: long jump, high jump, shot put, pole vault and so on.

## 17

**a. Stockholm.**

This was due to the Australian quarantine regulations and included dressage, eventing and show jumping.

## 18

**a. Berlin.**

Usually, the Olympics were followed by listening to the radio. The 1936 Berlin Olympics distinguished themselves by televising the events across the country.

# SPORTS WORDS

1. **In which sport can you score a 'turkey'?**
   a. Lacrosse
   b. Shinty
   c. Ten-pin bowling

2. **If you run out of energy while running you are said to... ?**
   a. Bonk
   b. Prang
   c. Zonk

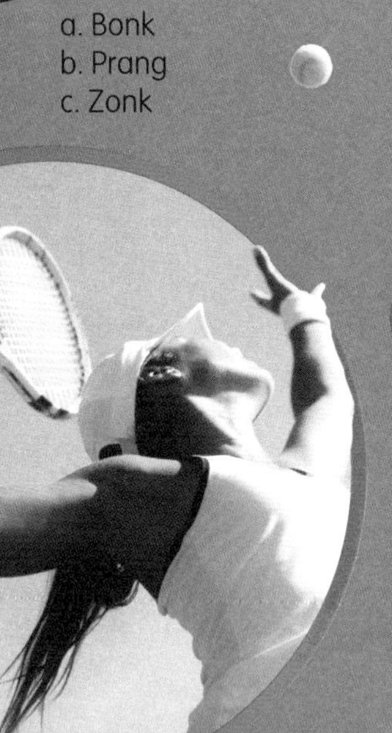

3. **In football, kicking the ball through your opponent's legs is called a...?**
   a. Basil
   b. Paprika
   c. Nutmeg

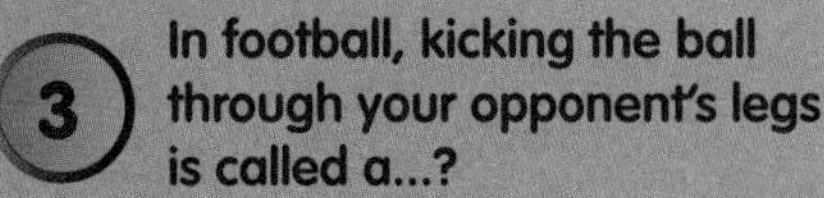

4. **Pepper is a popular warm-up sequence in which sport?**
   a. Volleyball
   b. Ice hockey
   c. Netball

5. **In tennis, a serve that is not returned is called what?**
   a. King
   b. Joker
   c. Ace

**6** **In which sport would you perform a slam dunk?**

a. Wrestling
b. Diving
c. Basketball

**7** **In ice hockey, why would teams 'face-off'?**

a. To end the game
b. To start the game
c. To substitute a player

**8** **Which of these best describes a 'dummy'?**

a. Pretending to pass
b. An unused substitute in a match
c. A referee who makes mistakes

**9** **Which of these is a Swedish training method to improve speed?**

a. Gaslek
b. Fartlek
c. Pumplek

**10** **In which sport can you score a 'bogey'?**

a. Fencing
b. Table tennis
c. Golf

# SPORTS WORDS

1 **c. Ten-pin bowling.**

This is where a player makes three strikes in a row!

2 **a. Bonk.**

Bonk is a condition of sudden fatigue, and loss of energy caused by lack of glycogen stores in the muscles.

3 **c. Nutmeg.**

It is called a 'salad' in Jamaica and a 'watermelon' in Cyprus.

4 **a. Volleyball.**

Usually played between two or three teammates. The idea is to pass, set, hit and then dig, set, hit in that order for as long as the players can control the ball.

5 **c. Ace.**

According to the International Tennis Hall of Fame, this term was created by a sports journalist named Allison Danzig. John Isner holds the record for most aces in a match, with 113.

**6** **c. Basketball.**

This shot is considered a field goal and worth 2 points in a game. The NBA holds an annual Slam Dunk Contest during the All-Star Weekend.

**7** **b. To start the game.**

One player is selected from each team to partake in the face-off in the centre of the rink. This occurs when the referee drops the puck between the sticks of the two opposing players.

**8** **a. Pretending to pass.**

This attacking play is valuable for evasion and used to break through defences in games.

**9** **b. Fartlek.**

Fartlek means 'speed play' in Swedish. It is unplanned bursts of fast running to a target point during a longer slower run.

**10** **c. Golf.**

This means the golfer made a score of one-over-par on an individual golf hole.

# FOOTBALL CRAZY

**1**

**When was the first Women's World Cup?**

a. 1990
b. 1991
c. 1992

**2**

**Brazilian forward Neymar holds which of these records?**

a. Most Champions League goals
b. Most international caps
c. Highest transfer fee

**3**

**Who is the English Premier League's all-time top scorer?**

a. Wayne Rooney
b. Harry Kane
c. Alan Shearer

**4**

**Which of these is a football team from Los Angeles?**

a. LA Galaxy
b. LA Rockets
c. LA Cosmos

**5**

**Which of these Scottish football teams plays in Glasgow?**

a. Hearts
b. Hibernian
c. Rangers

**6**

**How many teams competed in the first World Cup in 1930?**

a. 13
b. 16
c. 18

**7**

**What is the capacity of Wembley Stadium?**

a. 80,000
b. 85,000
c. 90,000

**8**

**El Clásico is a football match played between which teams?**

a. AC Milan and Inter Milan
b. Barcelona and Real Madrid
c. Ajax and Feyenoord

**9**

**Which former English footballer is co-owner of Inter Miami?**

a. David Beckham
b. Steven Gerrard
c. Frank Lampard

**10**

**Sadio Mané scored a Premier League hat-trick in what time?**

a. 4 minutes 56 seconds
b. 3 minutes 56 seconds
c. 2 minutes 56 seconds

**11**

**What nickname is given to Manchester United?**

a. The Red Devils
b. The Red Monsters
c. The Red Angels

**12**

**In which African country do Al Ahly play?**

a. Morocco
b. Egypt
c. Algeria

**13**

**Which of these is a real football team?**

a. Sleigh Bell FC
b. FC Santa Claus
c. Lapland United

**14**

**How long are goalkeepers allowed to hold the ball for?**

a. 12 seconds
b. 8 seconds
c. 6 seconds

**15**

**Which award did Megan Rapinoe win in 2019?**

a. FIFA Young Player of the Year
b. Ballon d'Or
c. Golden Glove

# FOOTBALL CRAZY

**1**

**b. 1991.**

The first tournament was held in China, and it featured 12 teams from six continents.

**2**

**c. Highest transfer fee.**

The transfer came in at a whopping 222 million euros!

**3**

**c. Alan Shearer.**

He scored 260 goals in the Premier League, which included 11 hat-tricks and 56 penalties.

**4**

**a. LA Galaxy.**

It was founded in 1994.

**5**

**c. Rangers.**

Rangers play at Ibrox Stadium in Glasgow. Hearts and Hibernian play their matches in Edinburgh.

**6**

**a. 13.**

This World Cup was won by Uruguay, which was also the host country. The tournament consisted of 18 games.

**7**

**c. 90,000.**

The 90,000-seat stadium reopened in 2007, after the original stadium was demolished.

**8**

**b. Barcelona and Real Madrid.**

The first El Clásico occurred 13 May 1902, where Barcelona won 3-1.

**9**

**a. David Beckham.**

They currently play in Fort Lauderdale while their new stadium, known as 'Miami Freedom Park', is being built.

**10**

**c. 2 minutes 56 seconds.**

This is the fastest hat-trick in Premier League history. Sadio Mané was playing for Southampton and scored the hat-trick against Aston Villa in 2015.

**11**

**a. The Red Devils.**

The official club mascot is called 'Fred the Red'. He sports two devil-like horns and a tail.

**12**

**b. Egypt.**

The club is known as 'The Club of the Century' in African football.

**13**

**b. FC Santa Claus.**

This football club is from Rovaniemi, Finland, and was formed in 1993.

**14**

**c. 6 seconds.**

The keeper can bounce the ball to reset the six seconds, but the referee can give them a card if it seems they are wasting time intentionally.

**15**

**b. Ballon d'Or.**

The award honours the football players deemed to have performed the best over the previous year, and is voted for by football journalists.

# KNOW YOUR TEAM

TRUE or FALSE

1. Utah Funk is a profesional basketball team.

2. Manchester Lightning compete in the Netball Superleague.

3. The England Women's Football Team is nicknamed the 'Lionesses'.

4. The Toronto Maple Leafs' team badge is a red maple leaf.

5. Kansas City Chiefs won the 2020 superbowl.

6. Eight cricket teams make up the Indian Premier League.

7. The Caribbean island of Jamaica has a bobsleigh team.

# QUIZ 51

**8**

Newcastle United are known as the 'Crows'.

**9**

Golf's Ryder Cup is contested between Team USA and Team Britain.

**10**

Korfball teams must have an equal number of males and females.

**11**

Toronto Blue Jays are a successful ice hockey team.

**12**

Cristiano Ronaldo played for Sporting Lisbon, Manchester United, Barcelona and Juventus.

**13**

The New Zealand rugby union team are known as the 'All Blacks'.

**14**

Sale Sharks are a rugby union team from Manchester.

**15**

Football club Independiente Caravel's logo features a pirate.

# KNOW YOUR TEAM

TRUE or FALSE

1

FALSE.
The NBA team for Utah is known as Utah Jazz.

2

FALSE.
The team is known as Manchester Thunder, and their senior players play in the Netball Superleague.

3

TRUE.
The team played, and won, its first official international match in November 1972 against Scotland.

4

FALSE.
The ice hockey team's logo was unveiled in 1927 and the maple leaf featured is navy blue.

5

TRUE.
This was their second Superbowl win, 50 years on from their first victory in 1970.

6

TRUE.
The Indian Premier League is the highest attended cricket league in the world.

7

TRUE.
The team made their debut in the 1988 Winter Olympic Games, where they were seen as the underdogs as they represented a tropical nation in winter sport. In 2018 Jamaica debuted their first women's bobsleigh team.

# QUIZ 51 ANSWERS

**8**

FALSE.
They are known as the Magpies from their famous black and white club colours.

**9**

FALSE.
It is Team USA and Team Europe who are pitted against each other in this tournament.

**10**

TRUE.
This sport originated in the Netherlands. Each team is comprised of eight players – four female and four male.

**11**

FALSE.
They are in fact a baseball team that competes in Major League Baseball.

**12**

FALSE.
He played for Real Madrid not Barcelona.

**13**

TRUE.
Some claim the name originated from a typing error of 'all backs' in a newspaper report.

**14**

TRUE.
The team was founded in 1861 and adopted the Sale Sharks name in 1999.

**15**

TRUE.
The Aruban football club is based in Angochi. The logo is yellow and blue.

# SUPER STADIUMS

**1**

**Which country plays rugby union at Murrayfield?**

a. England b. Wales
c. Scotland

**2**

**The Turkish football team Bursapor's stadium looks like a...?**

a. Crocodile b. Fortress
c. Castle

**3**

**The New York Knicks play at which stadium?**

a. Madison Circle Gardens
b. Madison Square Gardens
c. Madison Diamond Gardens

**4**

**What is the capacity of North Korea's Rungrado 1st of May Stadium?**

a. 94,000 b. 104,000
c. 114,000

**5**

**In India, which sport is played at the Sardar Patel Stadium?**

a. Field hockey
b. Cricket c. Rugby

**6**

**Which of these venues hosts tennis matches?**

a. Rotterdam Haha
b. Rotterdam Ahoy
c. Rotterdam Argh

**7**

**What is the name of FC Barcelona's home stadium?**

a. Camp Nou
b. Old Trafford
c. St James Park

**8**

**Which concert hall did Arnold Schwarzenegger win his final body building title in?**

a. Tyne Theatre Opera House
b. Sydney Opera House
c. Melbourne Theatre

**9**

**Where is the world's largest floating stage?**

a. Swaziland
b. Serbia
c. Singapore

**10**

**What is the roof of the London Olympic Stadium made of?**

a. Tiles
b. Polyester
c. Concrete

**11**

**What is the capacity of Wales' Principality Stadium?**

a. 7,450
b. 74,500
c. 745,000

**12**

**How much did it cost to build the first London Olympic Stadium in 1908?**

a. £1,000,000
b. £60,000 c. £300,000

**13**

**What is the name of the world's first multi-purpose, domed sports stadium?**

a. The NRG Astrodome
b. The Dome
c. Astrosphere

**14**

**Michigan Stadium is the largest stadium in the US. What is it also known as?**

a. The Church
b. The Big House
c. The Shed

**15**

**Which UK stadium has the highest capacity?**

a. Old Trafford
b. Wembley
c. Twickenham

# SUPER STADIUMS

**1**

**c. Scotland.**

It was first opened in 1925 and renovated in 1994.

**2**

**a. Crocodile.**

It has a capacity of 43,761 and was first opened in 2015.

**3**

**b. Madison Square Gardens.**

Since opening in 1968, the arena has hosted sporting events such as basketball and boxing.

**4**

**c. 114, 000.**

This stadium first opened in 1989 and has remained the largest stadium in the world. It occupies 51 acres of land.

**5**

**b. Cricket.**

This stadium is situated in the heart of Ahmedabad, and has a capacity of 110,000.

**6**

**b. Rotterdam Ahoy.**

This multi-purpose arena is located in Rotterdam, Netherlands. The Ahoy Arena was opened in 1971 and as of April 2019 it increased its seating capacity to 16,426.

**7**

**a. Camp Nou.**

This stadium can hold 99,354 people.

**8**

**b. Sydney Opera House.**

This UNESCO World Heritage site first opened in 1973.

**9**

**c. Singapore.**

The stage is located in Marina Bay and hosts both sporting and musical events.

**10**

**b. Polyester.**

It is designed to keep costs down, and some of the environmental impact down also.

**11**

**b. 74, 500.**

The stadium is situated in Cardiff, the country's capital, and is home to the Wales rugby union team.

**12**

**b. £60,000.**

This is quite a difference from the hundreds of millions spent building the stadium for the 2012 Summer Olympics.

**13**

**a. The NRG Astrodome.**

Located in Houston, Texas and opened in 1965. Unfortunately, in 2008 it was declared non-compliant with fire code regulations by the Houston Fire Department and parts of it were demolished in 2013.

**14**

**b. The Big House.**

This football stadium is for the University of Michigan's sporting events. It has a capacity of 107, 601!

**15**

**b. Wembley.**

Built in 2007, Wembley has a capacity of 90,000. Twickenham has 82,000 and Old Trafford has 76,000.

# WATER SPORTS

**1** **What was water polo originally called?**
a. Dive ball b. Aquatic football c. Splash Soccer

**2** **How many times has surfing been a sporting event in the Olympics?**
a. 0 b. 10 c. 20

**3** **Which of these water sports was used in World War II to gain higher vantage points?**
a. Parasailing b. Stand-up paddle boarding c. Snorkelling

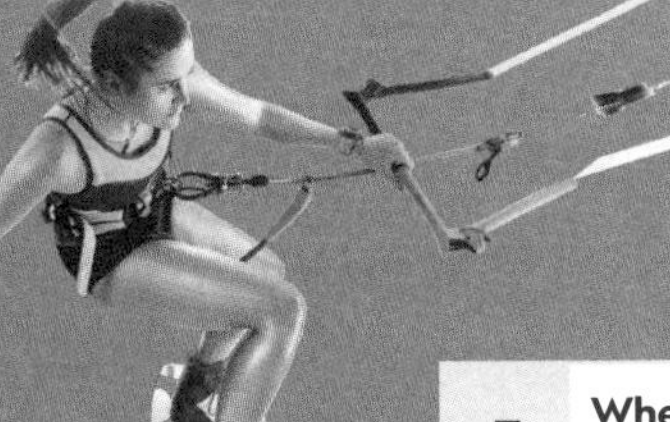

**4** **How long do kayaks date back?**
a. 100 years b. 600 years c. 4,000 years

**5** **When was water skiing invented?**
a. 1800 b. 1922 c. 1896

**6** **When did the first official surfing contest take place?**
a. 2001 b. 1928 c. 1950

**7** **Which is not a body position in diving competitions?**
a. Tuck b. Pen c. Pike

**8** **Which of these is not a water sport?**
a. Water basketball b. Aquathlon c. Parkour

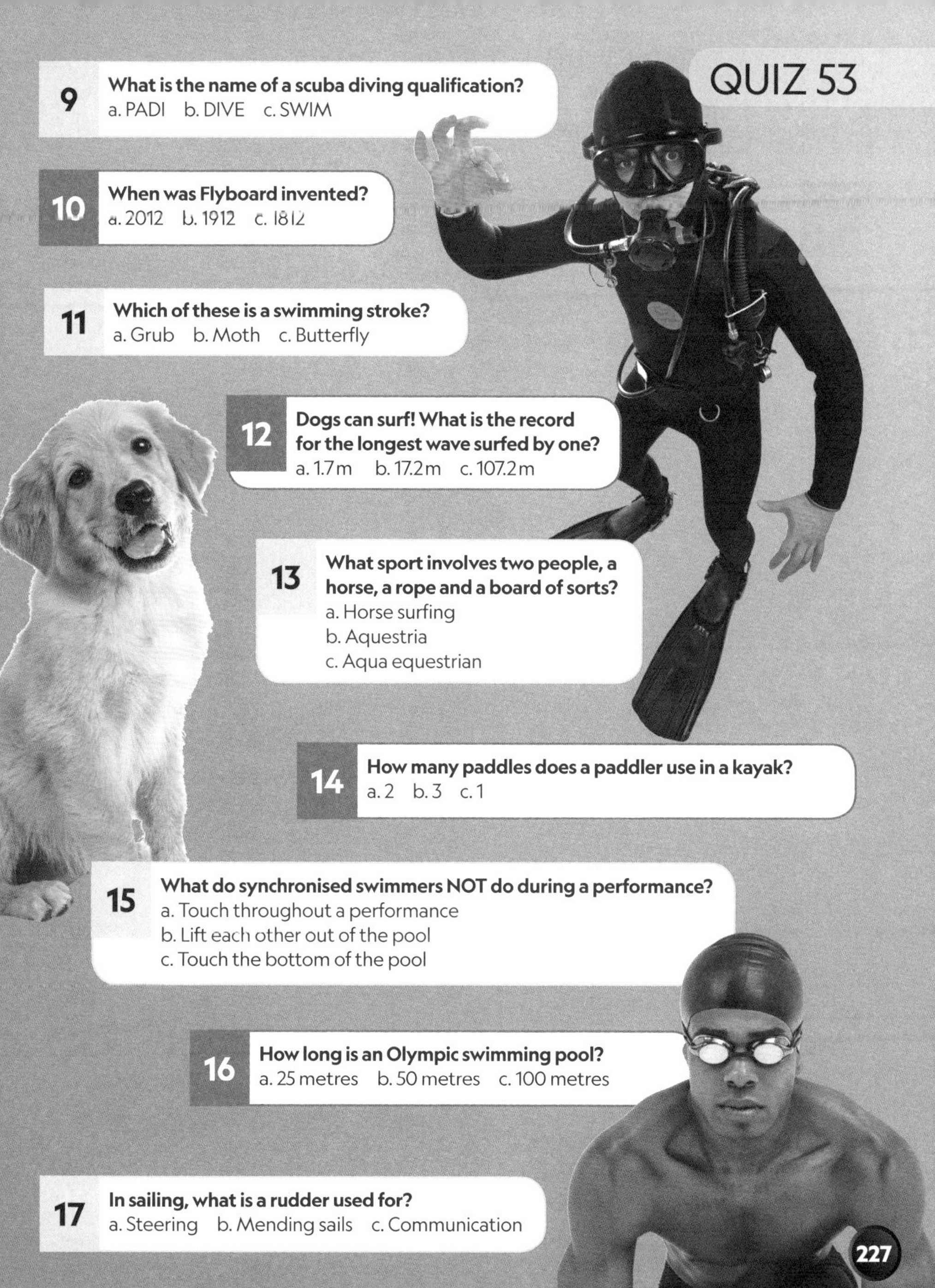

**9** **What is the name of a scuba diving qualification?**
a. PADI b. DIVE c. SWIM

**10** **When was Flyboard invented?**
a. 2012 b. 1912 c. 1812

**11** **Which of these is a swimming stroke?**
a. Grub b. Moth c. Butterfly

**12** **Dogs can surf! What is the record for the longest wave surfed by one?**
a. 1.7m b. 17.2m c. 107.2m

**13** **What sport involves two people, a horse, a rope and a board of sorts?**
a. Horse surfing
b. Aquestria
c. Aqua equestrian

**14** **How many paddles does a paddler use in a kayak?**
a. 2 b. 3 c. 1

**15** **What do synchronised swimmers NOT do during a performance?**
a. Touch throughout a performance
b. Lift each other out of the pool
c. Touch the bottom of the pool

**16** **How long is an Olympic swimming pool?**
a. 25 metres b. 50 metres c. 100 metres

**17** **In sailing, what is a rudder used for?**
a. Steering b. Mending sails c. Communication

# WATER SPORTS

**1** **b. Aquatic football.** The sport was created in the nineteenth century. It originated as a form of rugby/football played in rivers and lakes in England and Scotland.

**2** **a. 0.** The sport has never been a part of the Olympic Games, however it is due to feature for the first time at the Tokyo Games.

**3** **a. Parasailing.** Submarines would pull individuals behind them in order to gain a higher vantage point when observing enemies.

**4** **c. 4,000 years.** You can visit the world's oldest surviving kayaks in the North American section of the Five Continents Museum in Munich.

**5** **b. 1922.** It was invented when Ralph Samuelson used a pair of modified boards as skis and a sash cord as a towrope on Lake Pepin, Minnesota.

**6** **b. 1928.** It was held at Corona del Mar, California.

**7** **b. Pen.** There are four types of accepted body positions: tuck, pike, straight and free.

**8** **c. Parkour.** This is where a person moves rapidly through an area in an urban environment, jumping, climbing and running around obstacles.

# QUIZ 53 ANSWERS

**9** **a. PADI.** PADI stands for Professional Association of Diving Instructors and was founded in 1966.

**10** **a. 2012.** It was invented by a French water-craft rider, Franky Zapata. Flyboard is designed to allow the device (and the person controlling it) to elevate out of the water and move around in the air!

**11** **c. Butterfly.** Sometimes people refer to the butterfly stroke as 'the fly'.

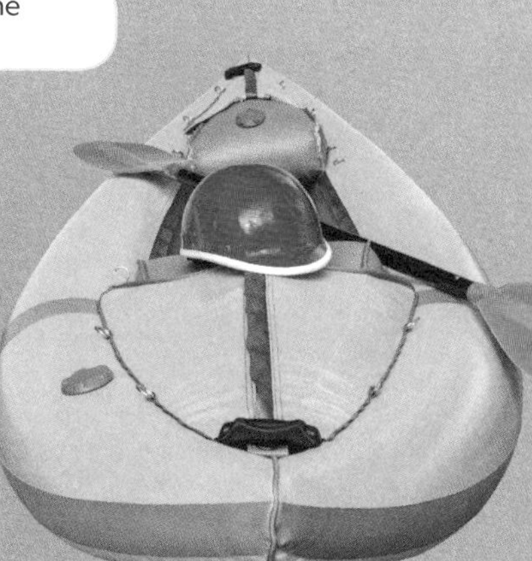

**12** **c. 107.2 metres.** Abbie Girl achieved this record at Ocean Beach Dog Beach in San Diego in 2011.

**13** **a. Horse surfing.** This extreme sport was invented in 2005 in England. The first competition was held in La Baul, France and has continued to grow in popularity internationally.

**14** **c. 1.** Kayaks are propelled by a double-bladed paddle. Some use single-bladed paddles too, depending on the kayak.

**15** **c. Touch the bottom of the pool.** Synchronised swimmers must continuously tread water like an eggbeater to create the illusion they are standing. If a swimmer touches the floor at any time, there is a two-point deduction.

**16** **b. 50 metres.** An Olympic swimming pool measures 50 metres long and 25 metres wide and is made up of 10 lanes.

**17** **a. Steering.** Rudders aren't just found in water vessels, planes have them too!

# SPORTING RECORDS

## TRUE or FALSE

**1**

Chris Froome is Britain's most successful Tour de France competitor.

**2**

Two rugby teams hold the record for most World Cup wins.

**3**

The fastest marathon time ever recorded is 2:01:39.

**4**

Liverpool have won more Champions League trophies than any other team.

**5**

The fastest time to complete a skydive on six continents was 8 days, 7 hours and 30 minutes.

**6**

Snowboarding down a mountain is faster than skiing.

**7**

Andy Murray has won more Wimbledon finals than Novak Djokovic.

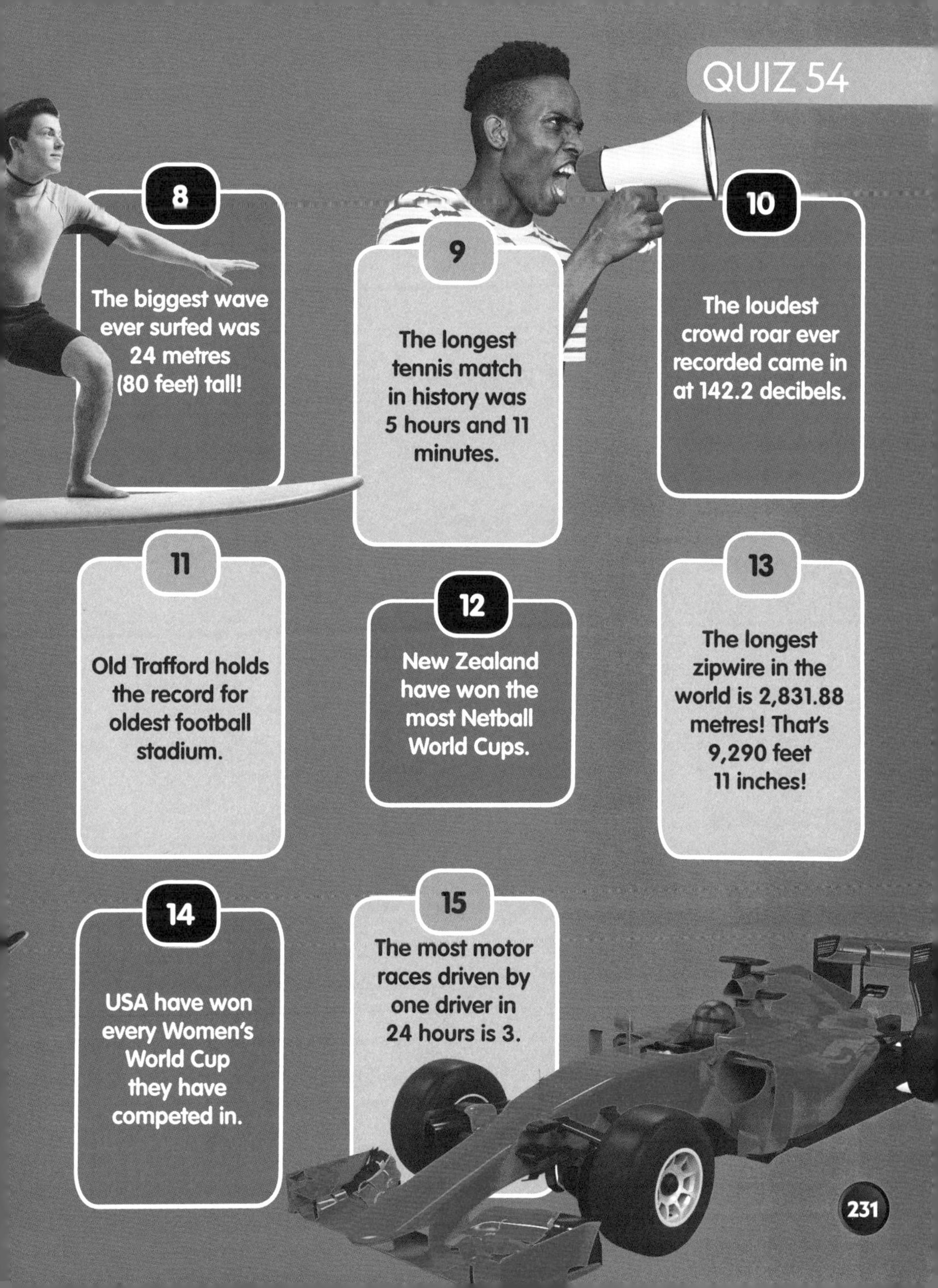

**8**

The biggest wave ever surfed was 24 metres (80 feet) tall!

**9**

The longest tennis match in history was 5 hours and 11 minutes.

**10**

The loudest crowd roar ever recorded came in at 142.2 decibels.

**11**

Old Trafford holds the record for oldest football stadium.

**12**

New Zealand have won the most Netball World Cups.

**13**

The longest zipwire in the world is 2,831.88 metres! That's 9,290 feet 11 inches!

**14**

USA have won every Women's World Cup they have competed in.

**15**

The most motor races driven by one driver in 24 hours is 3.

# SPORTING RECORDS

TRUE or FALSE

**1**

TRUE.
He has won 4 Tour de France races: 2013, 2015, 2016 and 2017.

**2**

TRUE.
These teams are New Zealand (1987,2011, 2015), and South Africa (1995, 2007, 2019).

**3**

TRUE.
The record was set at the Berlin Marathon in 2018 and is held by Kenyan runner Eliud Kipchoge.

**4**

FALSE.
The record is held by Real Madrid, who have been European champions 13 times.

**5**

TRUE.
This was achieved in 2008 by Martin Downs. The dives were completed in South Africa, Spain, Venezuela, USA, Australia and Vietnam.

**6**

FALSE.
The top speed for a skier downhill is 158.4mph (254.9 kmph), whereas for a snowboarder it is only 126.309 mph (203.275 kmph).

**7**

FALSE.
As of 2020, Murray has won two compared to Djokovic's five. Roger Federer has won eight times!

# QUIZ 54 ANSWERS

**8**

TRUE.
This record was set in 2017 by 38-year-old Rodrigo Koxa.

**9**

FALSE.
In 2010, John Isner and Nicolas Mahut played the longest professional match at Wimbledon. It lasted a whopping 11 hours and five minutes.

**10**

FALSE.
It was achieved by fans of the Kansas City Chiefs who beat New England Patriots in September 2014 at an American football game.

**11**

FALSE.
The oldest football ground is Sandgate, which is owned by Hallam FC in Sheffield. It was opened in 1860, and the first game was played on 26 December 1860.

**12**

FALSE.
Australia have won the most Netball World Cups – 11 times compared to New Zealand's five.

**13**

TRUE.
This record has been held since 2018 and can be found in Ras Al Khaimah!

**14**

FALSE.
They actually have a tournament win record of 50%, being crowned champions four times (1991, 1999, 2015, 2019).

**15**

FALSE.
Fiona Leggate completed 5 races at Silverstone Circuit in Northamptionshire on 25 July 2004.

# Magnificent MUSIC and the ARTS

**INTERNATIONAL BAGPIPE DAY** is celebrated annually on **10 MARCH.**

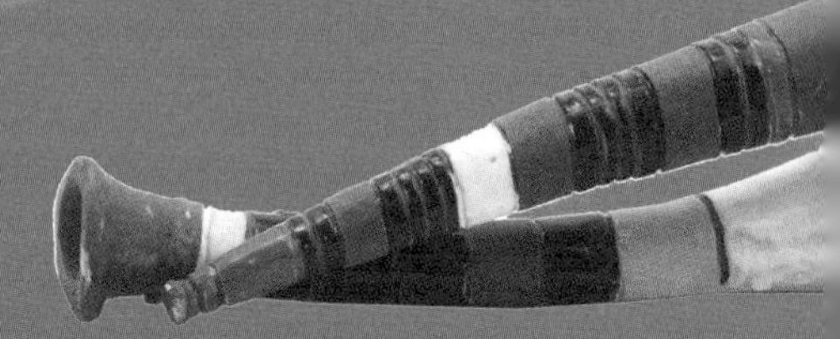

# CATEGORY 7

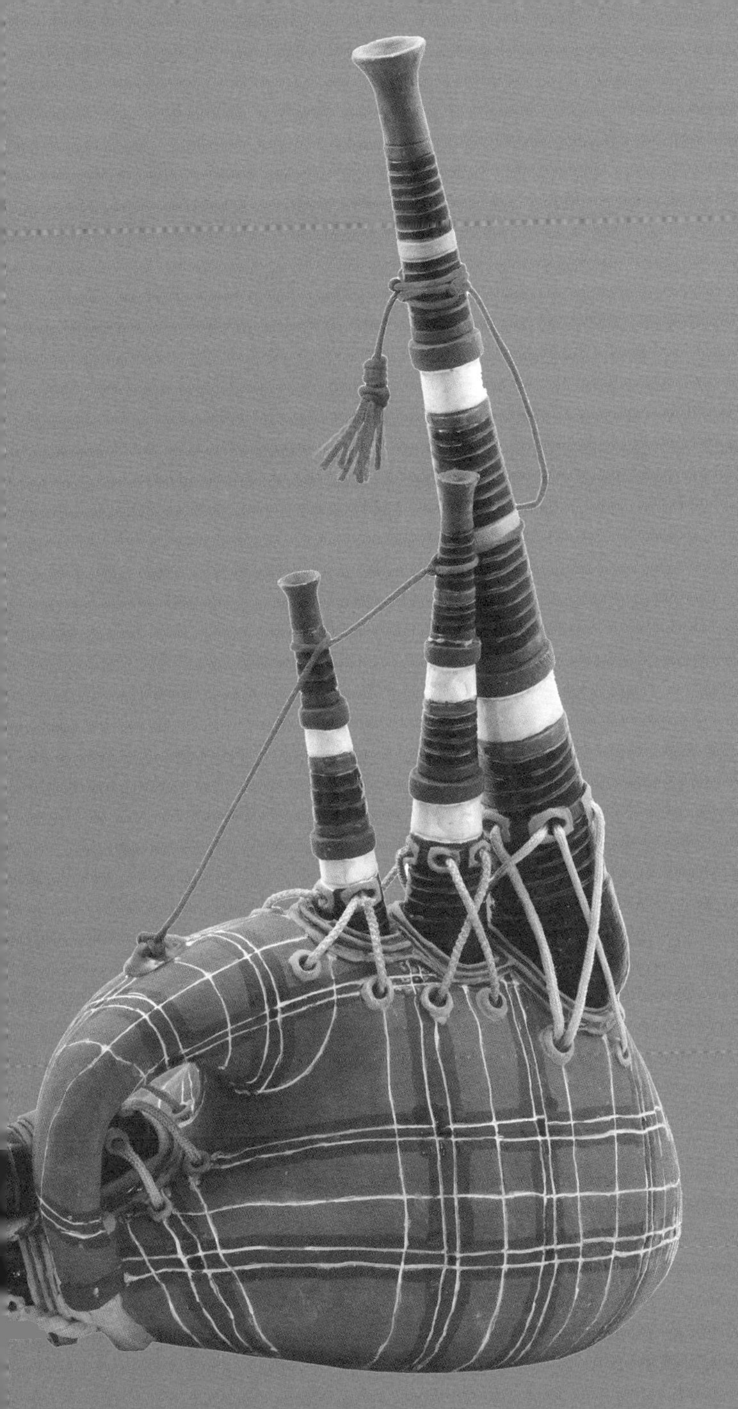

# MUSIC

**1** **What is a group of 50 to 100 classical musicians playing together called?**
a. A band b. An orchestra c. A trio

**2** **Ludwig van Beethoven was a famous composer with which disability?**
a. Blindness b. Paralysis c. Deafness

**3** **Which of these is an American singer?**
a. Taylor Swift b. Taylor Eagle c. Taylor Robin

**4** **What is a 'chord'?**
a. A type of song
b. A group of notes played together
c. A carrying strap for an accordion

**5** **Which one of these is a piece by Johann Sebastian Bach?**
a. Song for the Teapot
b. Air on the G String
c. Ode to the Violin

**6** **Which music type is performed on drums?**
a. Woodwind b. Percussion c. Wind

**7** **What do choir members do together?**
a. Play violins b. Play guitars c. Sing

**8** **In 1723, the Italian composer, Vivaldi, wrote four pieces of music named after what?**
a. The Four Seasons b. The Four Elements c. The Four Tops

**9** **Louis Armstrong is famous for playing which brass instrument?**
a. Trumpet b. Trombone c. Tuba

**10** **Bob Marley is associated with which style of music?**
a. Hip hop b. Reggae c. Heavy metal

**11** **Which of these is a style of music?**
a. Ragtime b. Moptime c. Brushtime

**12** **Freddie Mercury was the frontman for which famous rock band?**
a. Led Zeppelin b. Queen c. The Rolling Stones

**13** **What is opera?**
a. A style of singing
b. An instrument
c. A play where all the words are sung

**14** **Which pop song did NASA beam out into space towards Polaris, the North Star?**
a. Mr Blue Sky b. Across the Universe
c. Space Oddity

**15** **Which of these is a real British rap artist?**
a. Thunderz b. Stormzy c. Lightnin'

**DID YOU KNOW?**

**At 25 years old, Justin Bieber became the youngest artist to have seven number one albums in the USA.**

# MUSIC

**1** **b. An orchestra.** Modern orchestras have different sections for all the different types of instruments. The person who leads the musicians is called the conductor.

**2** **c. Deafness.** Beethoven lost most of his ability to hear when he was 44. Despite this, he continued to perform and conduct and is considered a genius of musical composition.

**3** **a. Taylor Swift.** As well as singing songs, Taylor Swift has starred in movies such as 'The Lorax' and 'Cats'.

**4** **b. A group of notes played together.** When the notes of a chord are played rapidly one after the other, it is called an arpeggio.

**5** **b. Air on the G String.** J.S. Bach wrote over 1,000 compositions during his life. He also had 20 children, four of whom grew up to be composers too.

**6** **b. Percussion.** This type of music is played by striking things by hand or with a beater. Drums are not the only percussion instrument: cymbals, xylophones, gongs, bells and shakers are also in the same family of instruments.

**7** **c. Sing.** Choir groups come in all shapes and sizes.

**8** **a. The Four Seasons.** The Four Seasons are four parts of a group of twelve concertos that Vivaldi titled 'The Trial between Harmony and Invention'.

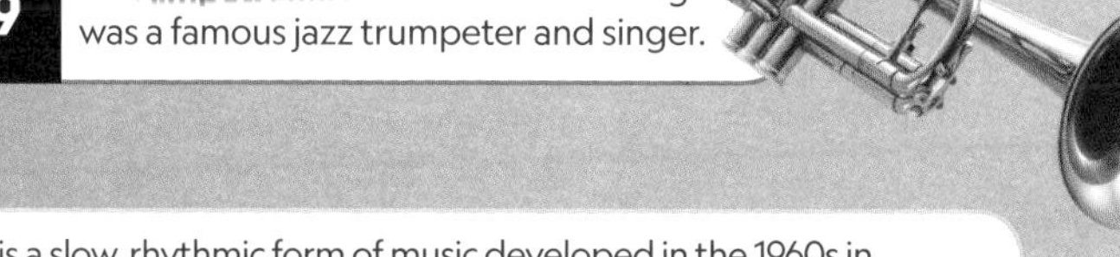

**9** **a. Trumpet.** Louis 'Satchmo' Armstrong was a famous jazz trumpeter and singer.

**10** **b. Reggae.** Reggae is a slow, rhythmic form of music developed in the 1960s in Jamaica. Bob Marley's songs include 'No Woman, No Cry' and 'Could You Be Loved'.

**11** **a. Ragtime.** Scott Joplin is perhaps the most famous ragtime composer. He wrote classics such as 'The Entertainer' and 'The Maple Leaf Rag'.

**12** **b. Queen.** Queen's rock anthem 'Bohemian Rhapsody' has repeatedly been voted best song of all time by millions of fans around the world.

**DID YOU KNOW?**

**War veteran, Captain Tom Moore, became the oldest person to have a number one hit in the UK. He was 99 years old!**

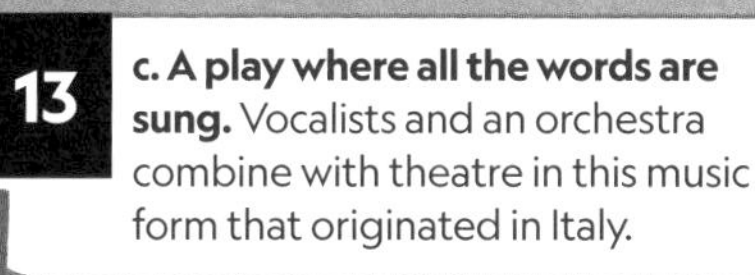

**13** **c. A play where all the words are sung.** Vocalists and an orchestra combine with theatre in this music form that originated in Italy.

**14** **b. Across the Universe.** Alongside 'Across the Universe', The Beatles' hits include 'She Loves You', 'Help!', 'Yellow Submarine', and 'I Am The Walrus'.

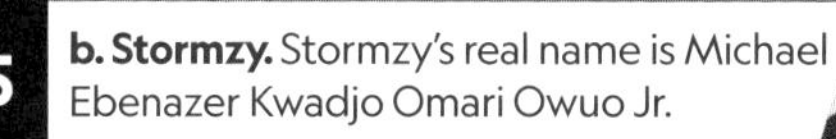

**15** **b. Stormzy.** Stormzy's real name is Michael Ebenazer Kwadjo Omari Owuo Jr.

# BOOKS

## 1

**Which book by Roald Dahl takes place in a seaside hotel, with a lot of very unpleasant guests?**

a. The Sorcerers
b. The Witches
c. The Hags

## 2

**Lewis Caroll wrote 'Alice's Adventures in Wonderland' and 'Through the Looking Glass,' but what was his other job?**

a. Physicist
b. Artist
c. Mathematician

## 3

**J.K. Rowling, the author of the Harry Potter series, is from which country?**

a. United Kingdom
b. Canada
c. USA

## 4

**Judith Kerr wrote a book called 'The Tiger Who Came to...'?**

a. Tea
b. School
c. Party

## 5

**What is the biggest library in the world?**

a. The British Library
b. The Library of Congress
c. Library and Archives Canada

## 6

**What is an autobiography about?**

a. A person's life
b. An ancient myth
c. A collection of animals

## 7

**Which of these are the most-read books in the world?**

a. Encyclopedias
b. Bibles
c. Atlases

# QUIZ 56

## 8

**Which country is considered to have invented the novel, as we know it?**

a. Japan
b. Peru
c. Kenya

## 9

**What is someone who reads a lot of books sometimes called?**

a. A paperfly
b. A readingbug
c. A bookworm

## 10

**Which brothers wrote some of the most famous fairy tales together?**

a. The Brothers Jimm
b. The Brothers Grimm
c. The Brothers Slimm

## 11

**How old is the printing press, which we use to create books?**

a. 580 years old
b. 1,000 years old
c. 925 years old

## 12

**What is the longest poem in the world?**

a. The Canterbury Tales
b. The Odyssey
c. The Mahabharata

## 13

**In the book 'The Hobbit' by J.R.R. Tolkien, what is the main character's name?**

a. Jumpo
b. Bilbo
c. Tricko

## 14

**How many different words are used in the story 'Green Eggs and Ham' by Dr. Seuss?**

a. 50
b. 150
c. 550

## 15

**What is the name for Japanese comic books and graphic novels?**

a. Janga
b. Manga
c. Fanga

# BOOKS

## 1

**b. The Witches.**

This famous children's story features a group of witches who meet at a hotel in order to make evil plans! It has been a very popular book since it was first written.

## 2

**c. Mathematician.**

Lewis Caroll is perhaps most famous for his children's books, but he originally studied mathematics. He was most interested in geometry and algebra.

## 3

**a. United Kingdom.**

J.K. Rowling finished writing the series in the Balmoral Hotel in Edinburgh. When her writing was complete, she signed a bust of the Greek god Hermes that was in her room.

## 4

**a. Tea.**

Author David Walliams narrated a TV adaptation of the book in 2019.

## 5

**b. The Library of Congress.**

With over 168 million volumes, The Library of Congress in Washington, D.C. is the world's largest library. It was established in 1800 and has books in over 450 languages!

## 6

**a. A person's life.**

An autobiography is the story of someone's life, that they have written themselves. It usually includes their experiences as a child and their grown-up life.

## 7

**b. Bibles.**

There are thousands of distinct manuscripts of the Christian bible, more than any other book!

## 8

**a. Japan.**

'The Tale of Genji' is widely considered to be the first real novel. It was written by a Japanese noblewoman in the early 11th century.

## 9

**c. A bookworm.**

We call someone a bookworm if they are always reading, but bookworms are also small larvae that eat paper as a food source. They are not actually worms at all!

## 10

**b. The Brothers Grimm.**

Jacob and Wilhelm Grimm were German academics with an interest in folklore. They collected stories from Europe in the 19th century, and wrote them down in their famous collection.

## 11

**a. 580 years old.**

In the 1440s, a German goldsmith named Johannes Gutenberg invented the first printing press. This made the production of books faster and more reliable.

## 12

**c. The Mahabharata.**

The Mahabharata is the world's longest poem. It was written in ancient India, and contains more than 1.8 million words, and over 100,000 verses!

## 13

**b. Bilbo.**

Bilbo Baggins is the main character in a book called 'The Hobbit.' He is a hobbit himself, a small creature who enjoys a comfortable life and lots of good food. Bilbo goes on some very big adventures in this story.

## 14

**a. 50.**

Interestingly, 49 of those 50 different words only have 1 syllable.

## 15

**b. Manga.**

One odd thing about manga books is that you read them back to front!

# ART

**1**

**Which artist, made famous by their street art, painted this?**

a. Wallsy b. Banksy
c. Shopsy

**2**

**Which 20th century artist made this screen-print portrait of actress Marilyn Monroe?**

a. Andy Warhol
b. Roy Liechtenstein
c. Pablo Picasso

**3**

**We've digitally blurred this painting. What is it called? Here's a clue: it's probably the most famous painting in the world.**

a. The Mona Lisa
b. The Starry Night
c. The Night Watch

**4**

**Which Itallian artist painted the ceiling of the Sistine Chapel?**

a. Leonardo da Vinci
b. Michelangelo
c. Raphael

**5**

**What is the name of this painting, which depicts a scene from the Bible?**

a. The Tower of Mabel
b. The Tower of Label
c. The Tower of Babel

**6**

**Where in the world is this style of art from?**

a. Russia
b. France
c. Japan

**7**

**What is the name of this paint-spattered bit of equipment, used by artists?**

a. Blender b. Pallette
c. Easel

**8**

**What is the name for the style of art shown in the painting above?**

a. Hidden art
b. Abstract art
c. Wheresthe art

**9**

Which of these is a special type of furnace, used for baking clay into pottery?

a. Hot box b. Kiln
c. Tandoor

**10**

The illustrator, John Tenniel, brought characters from which famous children's story to life?

a. Winnie the Pooh
b. Alice's Adventures in Wonderland
c. Animal Farm

**11**

What is the name of the artist who created the fantastic and surreal creatures in 'The Garden of Earthly Delights' shown here?

a. Calamitous Mosch
b. Hieronymous Bosch
c. Minodious Tosch

**12**

What is the paper-folding art from Japan called?

a. Shinto b. Origami
c. Ronbun

**13**

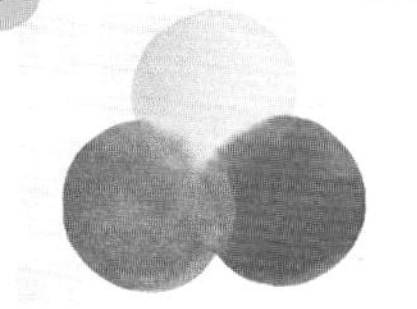

What is the collective name for the colours red, yellow and blue?

a. Base colours
b. First colours
c. Primary colours

**14**

A style of art that uses lots of individual dots of colour to make up the picture is known as what?

a. Dottyism b. Colourism
c. Pointilism

**15**

Which country of the United Kingdom is famous for its murals?

a. Northern Ireland
b. Scotland
c. Wales

**DID YOU KNOW?**

**Art competitions used to form part of the Olympic Games.**

# ART

**1**

**b. Banksy.**
One of Banksy's artworks sold for over $1 million at auction but was destroyed immediately afterwards by the artist, who activated a shredder hidden in the painting's frame.

**2**

**a. Andy Warhol.**
As well as producing other screen prints (of things such as cans of soup) Andy Warhol was also manager and producer for an influential 1960s rock band called The Velvet Underground.

**3**

**a. The Mona Lisa.**
Check out the original, which is kept at the Louvre Museum in Paris. Did you notice she doesn't have any eyebrows?

**4**

**b. Michelangelo.**
It took Michelangelo four years to complete. Painting a ceiling for that long took its toll on the artist, who wrote a poem about how much the job had hurt his back!

**5**

**c. The Tower of Babel.**
Bruegel is famous for the amazing detail he includes in his artworks. One reason they are so detailed is that, 450 years ago, fewer people could read and so the paintings were a way to tell a story without using words.

**6**

**c. Japan.**
The Japanese artist Katsushika Hokusai created this world-famous block printing called 'Under the Wave off Kanagawa', which shows Japan's Mount Fuji in the background.

**7**

**b. Pallette.**
Using only a few colours, artists mix and blend their paints on the pallette.

**8**

**b. Abstract art.**
Pablo Picasso is a world-famous artist who developed lots of art styles, including abstract art, through his paintings, sculptures, engravings and drawings.

# QUIZ 57 ANSWERS

**9**

**b. Kiln.**
Clay is a type of sticky earth that has been used as a building material to make bricks, bowls and other items for thousands of years.

**10**

**b. Alice's Adventures in Wonderland.**
It is hard to imagine Lewis Carroll's creations – such as the Cheshire Cat, and Tweedledum and Tweedledee – without picturing Tenniel's original illustrations.

**11**

**b. Hieronymous Bosch.**
The painting is called a triptych – a collection of three paintings on wooden panels; these were often used in churches and cathedrals as altarpieces.

**12**

**b. Origami.**
The art of paper folding goes back over a thousand years in Japan. Folding Orizuru – paper cranes – is a tradition, meant to bring peace and good luck.

**13**

**c. Primary colours.**
Primary colours can be mixed in different combinations to make all of the other colours.

**14**

**c. Pointilism.**
The French artist, Georges Seurat, made this style of art popular in the 19th century. Up close, these dotty paintings can look chaotic, but step back and the image appears.

**15**

**a. Northern Ireland.**
Murals are large pieces of art painted on walls and buildings.

**DID YOU KNOW?**

**The Mona Lisa receives so many letters that it has its own mailbox at the Louvre Museum.**

# MUSICAL INSTRUMENTS

**1** **As far as we know, how long have humans been playing musical instruments?**
a. 5,000 years b. 40,000 years c. 11,000 years

**2** **Which ancient brass instrument did a Danish farmer find buried in a peat bog.**
a. Lurs b. Jurs c. Durs

**3** **What is the name of the make of the most expensive violin ever sold?**
a. Rastafarius b. Stradivarius c. Othervarious

**4** **What is the Australian Aboriginal instrument, the Yidaki, more commonly known as?**
a. Didgeridoo b. Yowie c. Billabong

**5** **What is the name of the guitar-like instrument that uses a drum to amplify its sound?**
a. Ukelele b. Banjo c. Snare

**6** **What part of the body would you use to play a kazoo?**
a. Mouth b. Nose c. Hands

**7** **How many strings are there on a cello?**
a. 2 b. 4 c. 6

**8** **How many keys does a piano have?**
a. 99 b. 88 c. 66

# QUIZ 58

**9** **Where does the ukelele come from?**
a. Hawaii b. Monserrat c. Cuba

**10** **The djembe is a type of what?**
a. Bell b. Drum c. Rattle

**11** **Which of these is the name for an old type of trombone?**
a. Bagor b. Sackbut c. Netif

**12** **How many instruments are played in a quartet?**
a. 4 b. 6 c. 2

**13** **What letter of the alphabet is given to name the holes that can be seen on violins, violas, cellos and double basses?**
a. f b. z c. g

**14** **The saxophone, clarinet, oboe and bassoon all require this grassy item to play.**
a. Leaf b. Reed c. Bamboo

**15** **On what instrument might you find a 'whammy bar'?**
a. Drum kit b. Electric guitar c. Marimba

**DID YOU KNOW?**

**A balalaika is a russian guitar that has a triangle-shaped body and three strings.**

# MUSICAL INSTRUMENTS

**1** **b. 40,000 years.** While the earliest musical instruments date back 40,000 years, it is likely that the human voice was the first instrument, which dates back as far as we do.

**2** **a. Lurs.** Lurs were first uncovered by accident in the late 1700s when a farmer found long, curved and ancient brass horns in a peat bog. They are around 3,000 years old!

**3** **b. Stradavarius.** Antonio Stradivari was a master violin maker. Today, his 'Messiah' violin is worth an estimated $20 million.

**4** **a. Didgeridoo.** These instruments were originally created after people found thick eucalyptus tree branches that had been hollowed out by termites.

**5** **b. Banjo.** In the 1800s, banjos were a popular instrument in music from the southern USA.

**6** **a. Mouth.** A kazoo adds a buzzy sound to the player's voice when they hum or sing through it.

**7** **b. 4.** The name 'cello' is a shortened version of the instrument's full name 'violoncello', which means 'small large violin'.

**8** **b. 88.** The piano manufacturer, Steinway, developed what is now the standard 88 key piano in the 1884.

**9** **a. Hawaii.** The Hawaiian ukulele is actually an adaptation of an instrument called a machete guitar, which was introduced to the islands by settlers from Portugal.

**10** **b. Drum.** The African drum is said to be made of three spirits: that of the tree that the body of the drum is made of, the animal that the drum skin is made of, and the spirit of the person who made it .

**DID YOU KNOW?**

**'Piano' is a shortened version of the word 'pianoforte', which means soft (piano) and loud (forte).**

**11** **b. Sackbut.** The name 'Sackbut' is thought to come either from Middle French ('sacquer' – to pull; and 'bouter' - to push) or from Spanish ('sacar' – to pull; and 'bucha' – a tube).

**12** **a. 4.** A string quartet consists of two violins, a viola and a cello.

**13** **a. f.** F-holes help the sound inside the hollow body of the instrument to get out. They used to be called C-holes or S-holes.

**14** **b. Reed.** The reed is used in the mouthpiece of many woodwind instruments. It vibrates as the player blows air across it, which makes the sound.

**15** **b. Electric guitar.** Musicians famous for their electric guitar playing include Jimi Hendrix, Frank Zappa and Prince.

# GAMES

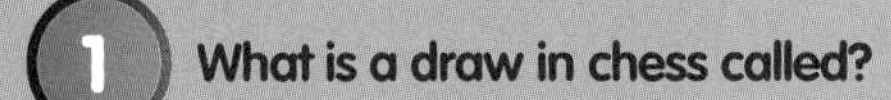

**1** **What is a draw in chess called?**

a. A stalepal
b. A stalefriend
c. A stalemate

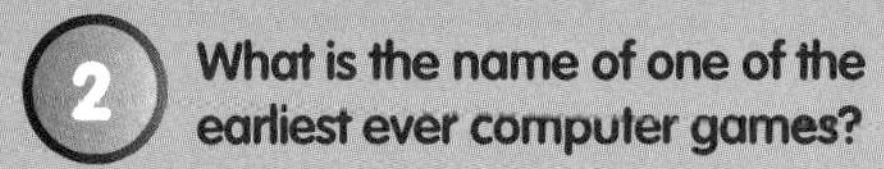

**2** **What is the name of one of the earliest ever computer games?**

a. Pong b. Stink c. Whiff

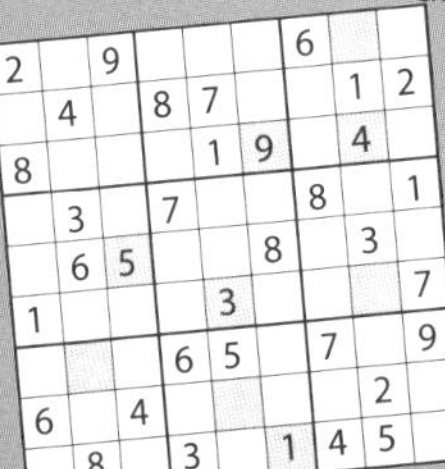

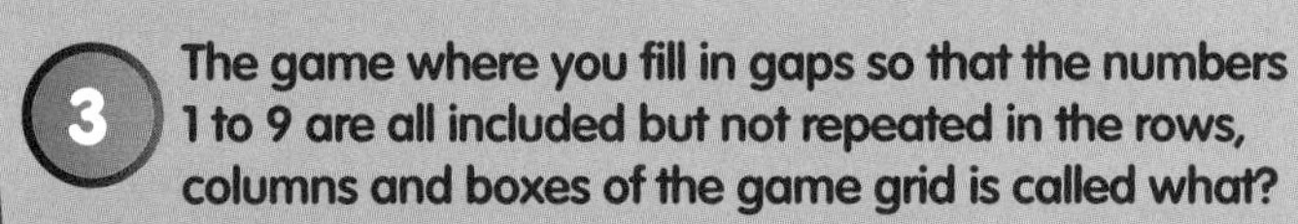

**3** **The game where you fill in gaps so that the numbers 1 to 9 are all included but not repeated in the rows, columns and boxes of the game grid is called what?**

a. Perogi b. Sudoku c. Umami

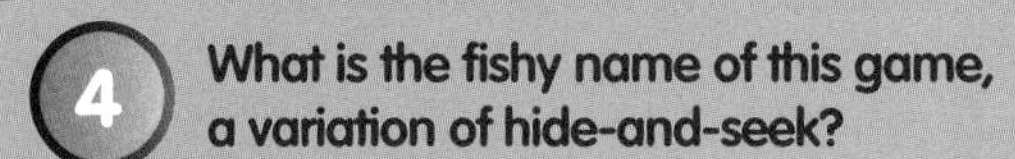

**4** **What is the fishy name of this game, a variation of hide-and-seek?**

a. Pilchards b. Mackerel c. Sardines

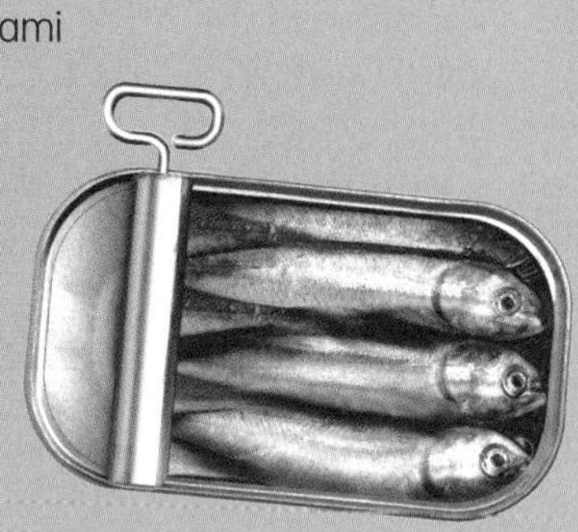

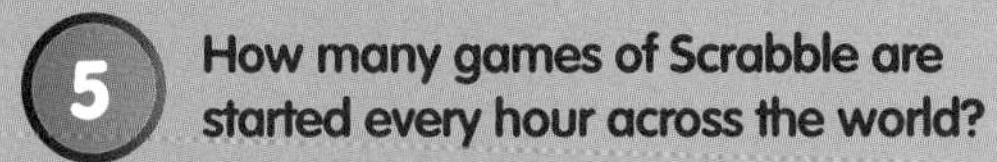

**5** **How many games of Scrabble are started every hour across the world?**

a. 5,000 b. 10,000 c. 30,000

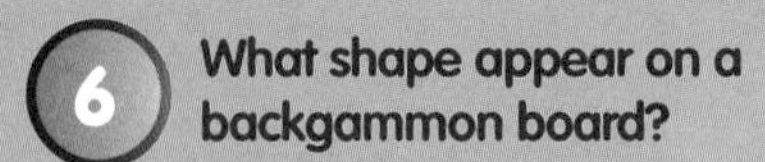

**6** **What shape appear on a backgammon board?**

a. Hexagons b. Traingles c. Pentagons

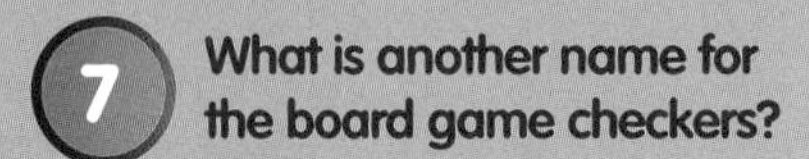

**7** **What is another name for the board game checkers?**

a. Draughts b. Breezes
c. Takeover

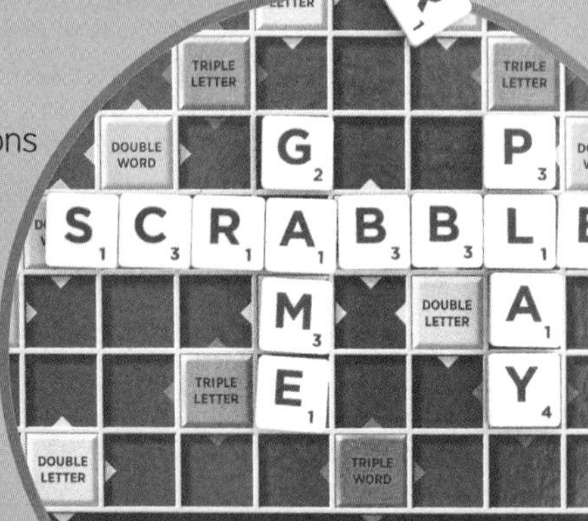

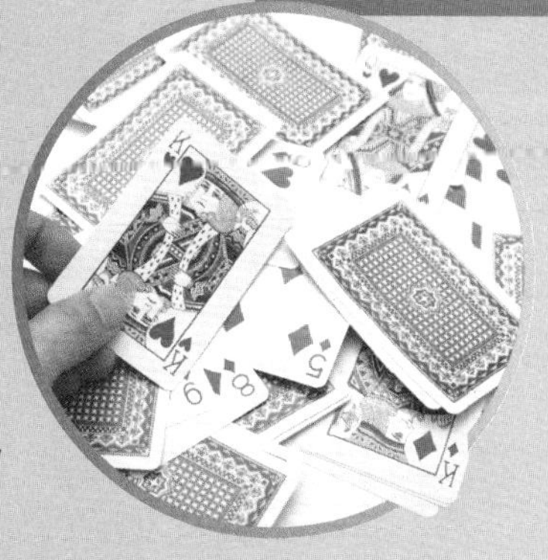

**8** **How many cards are there in a standard set of playing cards?**

a. 52 b. 51 c. 50

**9** **In what board game might you buy property, win second prize in a beauty contest, and go to jail?**

a. Mouse Trap b. Cluedo c. Monopoly

**10** **What is cribbage?**

a. A board game
b. A card game
c. A computer game

**11** **How many dominoes come in a set?**

a. 28 b. 30 c. 32

**12** **Which group game involves players sitting in a circle while another player goes around the outside, tapping each person on the head?**

a. Quack quack honk b. Duck duck goose c. Bird bird bird

**13** **Many people enjoy playing RPGs. What does RPG stand for?**

a. Run the public gauntlet
b. Really pretty good
c. Role-playing game

**14** **What was the board game Monopoly originally called?**

a. Bankruptcy!
b. The Landlord's Game
c. Money Money Money

**15** **What is another name for the card game 'Patience'?**

a. Lonely turnover
b. Solitaire
c. Suit collector

# GAMES

**1** **c. A stalemate.**
The objective in chess is to capture the other player's king, which is called checkmate. If the king of the player whose turn it is is not threatened by the next move but there is no legal move they can make, there is 'stalemate' which is a kind of draw.

**2** **a. Pong.**
Despite being released in the early 1970s, people enjoy playing this ping-pong arcade game to this day.

**3** **b. Sudoku.**
These puzzles require logic to solve and have difficulties ranging from simple to fiendishly difficult.

**4** **c. Sardines.**
In sardines, when a player finds someone hiding, they have to squeeze into the same hiding place!

**5** **c. 30,000.**
Scrabble was invented in 1933 by an American architect called Alfred Mosher Butts

**6** **b. Triangles.**
Archaeologists have uncovered backgammon sets in Turkey and Iran that date back over 5,000 years.

**7** **a. Draughts.**
If a game of draughts is played perfectly between both players, the game should end in a draw.

## QUIZ 59 ANSWERS

**8** **a. 52.**
A deck of cards is split into 4 groups, called 'suits': clubs, diamonds, hearts and spades. Each suit has 13 cards in it. 4 x 13 = 52. Decks also include 2 joker cards.

**9** **c. Monopoly.**
The Monopoly playing pieces, which include a top hat, a dog and a boot, were updated in 2013 with the inclusion of a cat playing piece.

**10** **b. A card game.**
Cribbage – or crib – is a popular two-player card game. Some of its sayings are now used in everyday English, such as 'level pegging' and 'streets ahead'.

**11** **a. 28.**
As well as being a number-matching game, dominoes are also used to create a domino effect where a line of dominoes is toppled over.

**12** **b. Duck duck goose.**
Other traditonal playground games include Blind Man's Buff, What's the Time Mister Wolf?, and Hopscotch.

**13** **c. Role-playing game.**
Role-playing games, such as Dungeons & Dragons, encourage players to use their imaginations and creativity to make the game up as they go along.

**14** **b. The Landlord's Game.**
Lizzie Magie, who patented The Landlord's Game in the early 1900s, wanted the game to show how horrible landlords could be in taking advantage of their tenants.

**15** **b. Solitaire.**
There are many variations of this game. In some, when completed, the deck of cards is sorted into suits and put in order.

# THEATRES AND MUSEUMS

## TRUE or FALSE

1

A sloping stage is called a 'fork'.

2

Shakespeare built his own theatre.

3

To wish an actor luck before going on stage, you should say 'Break a leg!'

4

The Lion King, which has been adapted into a lavish musical extravaganza, is based on Shakespeare's 'Hamlet'.

5

A trapdoor is a type of pyrotechnic (which means fiery!) special effect, sometimes used in theatrical productions.

6

Disneyworld in the US state of Florida has over 3 million costumes in its theatrical wardrobes.

7

There is a museum in Germany that is filled with dead bodies of real people.

8

In India, there is a museum all about the toilet.

9

There's a museum in Mexico that is completely underwater.

10

A museum in Japan is dedicated to instant noodles.

11

The Palace Theatre in London, UK, has seats that are reserved for ghosts.

12

The word 'Theatre' comes from the Greek for 'Goat Song'.

13

There is a museum in Kansas in the United States that is entirely devoted to fences.

14

The longest-running play in the world is called 'The Mousetrap'.

15

Instead of clapping, Ancient Greeks would show their appreciation for a performance by stomping their feet.

DID YOU KNOW?

There is an underwater museum in Cancun, Mexico.

# THEATRES AND MUSEUMS

TRUE or FALSE

**1**

FALSE.
Stages are sometimes sloped so that the audience can see more of what's going on. This is called a 'rake'.

**2**

TRUE.
The Globe theatre was built by Shakespeare and his company of actors over 400 years ago.

**3**

TRUE.
It is actually considered bad luck to have somebody wish you 'good luck' before going on stage. Actors have many superstitions.

**4**

TRUE.
Both stories centre around a young prince who loses his father, leaves his kingdom, and has to return to set things right.

**5**

FALSE.
A trapdoor is a door that's hidden in the stage floor. The people behind the scenes can then make anything on stage disappear.

**6**

FALSE.
Despite not having 3 million, Disneyworld still has well over 1 million costumes, including Snow White, Cinderella and Rapunzel.

**7**

TRUE.
The Plastinarium in Guben, Germany, features the bodies of people and animals preserved using plastic. It is a rather grisly, but educational, way to learn about anatomy!

**8**

TRUE.
Over 4,500 years of the history of humans and toilets can be found at the Sulabh International Museum of Toilets!

**9**

TRUE.
Visitors can either look at the museum through the floor of a glass-bottomed boat, or they can snorkel or Scuba dive to explore nearly 500 sculptures on the sea floor.

**10**

TRUE.
The museum features a tunnel of ramen, in which visitors get to see the history of instant noodle snacks.

**11**

TRUE.
Well, they used to, until a performance of a Harry Potter play meant that the ghosts had to stand and watch!

**12**

FALSE.
Theatre means 'to behold' in Ancient Greek. 'Goat song' in Ancient Greek, is where the word 'tragedy' comes from!

**13**

FALSE.
There is, however, a museum in Kansas devoted to barbed wire!

**14**

TRUE.
The play is a murder mystery, from a short story written by author Agatha Christie.

**15**

TRUE.
The oldest play in the world is called 'The Persians' and was written about 2,500 years ago.

**DID YOU KNOW?**

Minack Theatre in Cornwall is an outdoor theatre carved into a granite cliff.

# AT THE MOVIES

**1** **What was the first movie to be made entirely using computer generated imagery (CGI)?**

a. Toy Story b. A Bug's Life c. Cars 2

**2** **'Jaws' is a movie about which sea-dwelling animal?**

a. Giant octopus b. Great white shark c. Water bear

**3** **Which of these is the title of a movie in which a massive ocean liner hits an iceberg and sinks?**

a. The Poseidon Adventure b. Speed II: Cruise Control c. Titanic

**4** **The style of animation, in which a model is photographed, moved ever-so-slightly, then photographed again, is called what?**

a. Cell-shaded animation b. Stop-motion animation c. No-time animation

**5** **Someone who adds sound effects to movies is called what?**

a. A Foley artist b. A Moley artist c. A Koley artist

**6** **Which fictional character has had the most movies made about them?**

a. Batman b. Sherlock Holmes c. James Bond

**7**

**How short is the shortest movie ever nominated for an Academy Award?**

a. 100 seconds b. 200 seconds c. 500 seconds

**8**

**Cinema originated in which country?**

a. UK b. France c. USA

**9**

**Which series of movies each start with the words, 'A long time ago, in a galaxy far, far away...'**

a. Star Wars b. Harry Potter c. The Avengers

**10**

**Which of these were a pair of famous comedians in the early black and white days of movies?**

a. Penn and Teller
b. Laurel and Hardy
c. Tom and Jerry

**11**

**Sales of which type of pet increased after the release of the movie 'Finding Nemo'?**

a. Parrotfish b. Clownfish
c. Seahorses

**12**

**'Tombstone', 'The Good, The Bad and the Ugly' and 'True Grit' are what sort of movies?**

a. Westerns
b. Science fiction
c. Horror

**13**

**'Let it Go' is an award-winning song from which chilly animated movie?**

a. Happy Feet b. Ice Age
c. Frozen

**14**

**Complete this movie-related phrase: 'Lights, Camera...'**

a. ...Cut! b. ...Lunch!
c. ...Action!

**15**

**In movie credits there are some odd job titles. Which of these is a real job on a movie set?**

a. Dolly grip b. Bear hug
c. Toy hold

# AT THE MOVIES

| | |
|---|---|
| 1 | **a. Toy Story.** Computer graphics had been seen in films before Toy Story, but this was the first time that a whole, full-length movie was made with CGI. |
| 2 | **b. Great white shark.** The author of 'Jaws' came to regret making so many people afraid of sharks. He thought humans were much more dangerous than these beautiful fish. |
| 3 | **c. Titanic.** One of the most successful films of all time, 'Titanic' is based on real-life tragic events. In 1912, on its first-ever voyage, the Titanic sank to the bottom of the Atlantic Ocean, with the loss of over a thousand lives. |
| 4 | **b. Stop-motion animation.** Examples of stop-motion animated movies include 'Fantastic Mr. Fox', 'Coraline' and 'Wallace and Gromit'. |
| 5 | **a. A Foley artist.** Foley artists use ingenious techniques to create sounds heard in movies. To recreate the sound of shoes walking in snow, they press shoes into cornstarch, or squeeze it in a leather pouch and record the sound. |
| 6 | **b. Sherlock Holmes.** Sir Arthur Conan Doyle wrote 60 stories about the detective Sherlock Holmes and his assistant, Watson, but there have been over 200 movies! |
| 7 | **a. 100 seconds.** The movie is called 'Fresh Guacamole' which makes sense: in a movie less than 2 minutes long there is no time for it to go off! |

| | |
|---|---|
| 8 | **b. France.** Brothers Auguste and Louis Lumière invented the Cinematograph in 1895 – the first camera that could record, develop and project movies! |
| 9 | **a. Star Wars.** Star Wars day is celebrated on 4 May because the date sounds like the movie line 'May the force be with you.' |
| 10 | **b. Laurel and Hardy.** Oliver Hardy started out his career playing villains, until he teamed up with Stan Laurel. Together they made over 100 slapstick comedies. |
| 11 | **b. Clownfish.** This resulted in damage to the wild clownfish population as many were removed from their natural habitats. |
| 12 | **a. Westerns.** In the 1960s, many 'spaghetti' westerns (which were set in the wild west of America, but filmed in the deserts of Spain) starred Clint Eastwood and featured haunting guitar themes by composer Ennio Morricone. |
| 13 | **c. Frozen.** The story of 'Frozen' was inspired by the fairy tale 'The Snow Queen' by Hans Christian Andersen. |
| 14 | **c....Action!** The phrase refers to letting the lighting people know first to switch on the lights, secondly for the camera crew to get their cameras rolling, and third, for the actors to get acting! |
| 15 | **a. Dolly grip.** Someone who is a dolly grip is responsible for moving the cranes and wheeled platforms that cameras are sometimes mounted on. |

# Fabulous FOOD

# CATEGORY 8

Machine-spun
**CANDY FLOSS**
was **INVENTED**
in the late
**19TH-CENTURY** by
William Morrison...
a **DENTIST!**

# WORLD FOODS

TRUE or FALSE

1

Rice plants feed half the world.

2

Leeks are a symbol of Northern Ireland.

3

Australians eat 'Flake and chips' which is seagull and chips.

4

Camel milk is more widely drunk than cow milk in some parts of Africa and the Middle East.

5

In Japan, certain fruits are considered to be luxury gifts, they are grown in odd shapes and imperfect.

6

Carrots are grown throughout Antarctica.

7

British sailors were referred to as 'limeys' because of their citrus diet.

8

Ackee fruit, popular in Jamaica, is always safe to eat.

9

Rhubarb leaves are poisonous.

10

In hot climates, an orange doesn't grow with orange skin, it's green!

# QUIZ 62

**11**

Durian fruit is banned on public transport in Singapore.

**12**

Chefs need to have a licence to prepare the Japanese delicacy, fugu (pufferfish).

**13**

Shrove Tuesday is known as Pancake Day all over the world.

**14**

You can get eel flavoured ice cream in Japan.

**15**

One of the most popular pizza toppings in Brazil is green peas.

**16**

Cornish pasties gets their name from its corn filling.

**17**

Mexico drinks the most Coca-Cola in the world.

**18**

Finland drinks the most tea in the world.

**19**

Scotland's national dish comes from a wild animal called a 'haggis'.

**20**

In Colombia, a popular cinema snack is dried ants!

# WORLD FOODS

## TRUE or FALSE

**1**

TRUE.
Rice is the staple food for 3.5 billion people around the globe.

**2**

FALSE.
The root vegetable isn't a symbol of Northern Ireland but it is an emblem of Wales.

**3**

FALSE.
'Flake and chips' is in fact an Australian dish, but 'flake' is actually shark.

**4**

TRUE.
Camlels can go for long periods without water and can still produce milk after not drinking for 7 days.

**5**

FALSE.
Some farmers grow perfect fruit, and they are considered luxury gifts. Two perfect melons can cost thousands of pounds.

**6**

False.
Carrots are native to Europe and Asia. Did you know that carrots aren't just orange. They come in lots of colours, including purple, white and black!

**7**

TRUE.
The Navy required sailors to consume limes to protect them against scurvy, a deadly disease that killed sailors on long sea journeys.

**8**

FALSE.
Eating some parts can be deadly! The mature fruit will break open naturally, exposing a ripe flesh; that is safe to eat once the black seeds have been removed.

**9**

TRUE.
Rhubarb leaves can be fatal if eaten.

# QUIZ 62 ANSWERS

**10**

TRUE.
Unless oranges experience a cool spell of weather, their skin will remain green.

**11**

TRUE.
Durian is banned on public transport because of its offensive strong stench!

**12**

TRUE.
You need to be specially trained to remove the poisonous parts of the pufferfish.

**13**

FALSE.
It has a number of different names! In Iceland it's called 'Sprengidagur' (meaning 'Bursting Day').

**14**

TRUE.
Eel is a popular delicacy in Japan in the summer, so you can kind of see how they came up with eel ice cream!

**15**

TRUE.
Pizzas may also be spinkled with carrots, beetroots and raisins!

**16**

FALSE.
They come from Cornwall, hence the name Cornish pasty. They are filled with beef, turnip, potato and onion.

**17**

TRUE.
Mexicans drink more Coca-Cola products than any other nation.

**18**

FALSE.
It is actually Turkey that drinks the most tea out of any country. They even beat out the Brits for the top spot!

**19**

FALSE.
The national dish is haggis (a pudding of sheep offal, onion and spices) but it is not a wild animal!

**20**

TRUE.
Dried ants are a popular alternative to popcorn with Colombians!

# FRUIT AND VEG

1 **Where are kiwi fruits native to ?**
a. China b. Greece c. New Zealand

2 **How many types of bananas are there?**
a. 20 b. 250 c. 1000

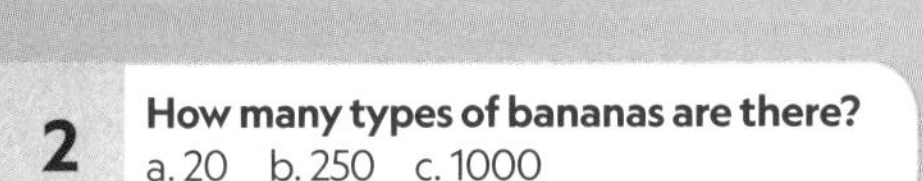

3 **Approximately how many seeds does a strawberry have?**
a. 200 b. 300 c. 400

4 **What berry can also be black, purple or gold?**
a. Strawberry b. Raspberry c. Blackberry

5 **What are pumpkins?**
a. Fruits b. Vegetables c. Flowers

6 **Which country supplies most of Europe's pineapples?**
a. South Africa b. Brazil c. Costa Rica

7 **What fruit is 96% water?**
a. Cucumber b. Bananas c. Oranges

8 **What fruit is roughly 20% air?**
a. Bananas b. Apples c. Limes

9 **What plant family does lettuce belong to?**
a. Rose b. Sunflower c. Lily

10 **What dried fruit has the most calcium content?**
a. Apricot b. Bananas c. Figs

**11** **Gala, Fuji and Granny Smith are types of...?**
a. Apples b. Oranges c. Bananas

**12** **What continent is corn NOT grown in?**
a. Africa b. Antarctica c. South America

**13** **Where did The Vegetable Orchestra first originate?**
a. Venice b. Barcelona c. Vienna

**14** **Some fruits give off a gas called ethylene. What happens to other fruits that come into contact with this gas?**
a. They ripen faster b. They shrink c. They die

**15** **What fruit can replace eggs when baking cakes?**
a. Oranges b. Bananas c. Grapes

**16** **What was the first vegetable to be grown in space?**
a. Potatoes b. Carrots c. Turnips

**17** **What fruit is a clone?**
a. Bananas b. Apples c. Pears

**18** **What fruit has been grown square-shaped in Japan?**
a. Watermelon b. Pineapple c. Oranges

**19** **What does a pattypan squash resemble?**
a. A plane b. A flying saucer c. A boat

**20** **What vegetable is carved in Oaxaca, Mexico for the Noche De Rábanos celebration?**
a. Radishes b. Turnips c. Onions

# FRUIT AND VEG

**1** **a. China.** China – where they are known as monkey peaches.

**2** **c. 1000.** Varieties include Cavendish, Lady Finger and Plantain.

**3** **a. 200.** On average, each strawberry will have 200 seeds. They are the first fruit to ripen in spring!

**4** **b. Raspberry.** Raspberries like cool, temperate climates and can be grown in a variety of colours and with different flavours.

**5** **a. Fruits.** Fruit is the fleshy part of a plant that contains the seeds so peppers, tomatoes and cucumbers are considered to be fruits too!

**6** **c. Costa Rica.** Approximately 75% of Europe's pineapples come from the Central American country.

**7** **a. Cucumber.** They are lower in nutrients but their high water content makes them a great fruit to have in the summer! Thei water percentage is followed closely by celery and tomatoes.

**8** **b. Apples.** While this fruit is filled with juicy flavours that come from the water, sugars and acids within, the spaces between the cells are filled with air and this is why they floa in water, and we can play the popular apple bobbing gam

**9** **b. Sunflower.** The sunflower family is also known as the daisy family.

**10** **c. Figs.** They are higher in calcium than any other dried fruit.

# QUIZ 63 ANSWERS

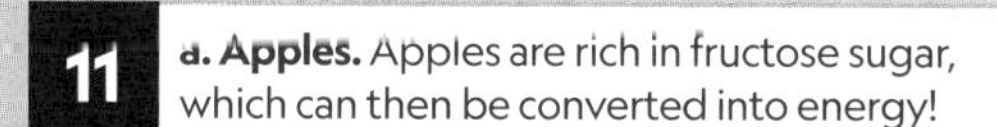

**11** **a. Apples.** Apples are rich in fructose sugar, which can then be converted into energy!

**12** **b. Antarctica.** The climate conditions in this continent are not suitable for the growth of corn.

**13** **c. Vienna.** This is a musical group who use instruments made entirely from fresh vegetables.

**14** **a. They ripen faster.** This can be helpful but can also mean that your fruit will go off before you get a chance to eat it.

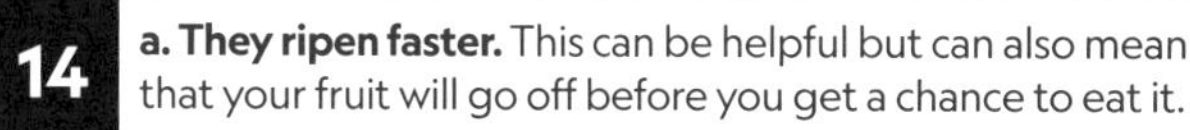

**15** **b. Bananas.** You could also use mashed potato, prune puree and some others! These ingredients help give the cakes a fluffy texture and bind ingredients, like eggs do.

**16** **a. Potatoes.** This was first tested in October 1995 aboard the Space Shuttle Columbia. The growth of plants on long space missions is important in providing food and water, as well as replenishing oxygen.

**17** **a. Bananas.** The only kind of dessert banana that is sold in UK shops is Cavendish. This variety of banana is a clone, which means they all have the same genes.

**18** **a. Watermelon.** These were developed by growing watermelons in glass boxes in order for them to grow into a cube shapes.

**19** **b. A flying saucer.** Also known as a scallop squash, it comes in a variety of colours such as white, yellow and green.

**20** **a. Radishes.** Each year, on 23 December, people create the most beautiful carvings and art out of radishes to celebrate 'Night of the Radishes'. The most beautiful carvings are bought as centrepieces for Christmas dinner tables.

# SWEET TREATS

## TRUE or FALSE

**1**
In some parts of the USA, you can find vending machines that dispense cupcakes.

**2**
In New York, there are more Starbucks than Dunkin' outlets.

**3**
The average Swiss person eats 5 kg of chocolate every year!

**4**
When machine-produced candy floss was first introduced it was originally called fairy floss.

**5**
Beef tongue is a popular ice cream flavour in Ireland.

**6**
In Arizona, you can buy caramel apples dipped in mealworms!

**7**
If you swallow chewing gum it takes 7 years to digest!

**8**

You can jazz up your ice-cream sandwiches with sweetcorn flavoured ice-cream!

**9**

White chocolate is made with white cocoa beans.

**10**

A 99 ice-cream is named after its price!

**11**

There are more than 400 million M&M's produced every day!

**12**

Jelly Babies were once named 'Peace Babies'.

**13**

Wine gums contain alcohol.

**14**

The Snickers bar got its name from its inventor's family horse.

**15**

The world's largest lollipop was more than 5 metres tall (with the stick).

# SWEET TREATS

TRUE or FALSE

**1**

TRUE.
One company has machines in many states including California, Arizona and Texas.

**2**

FALSE.
In 2019 there were more Dunkin's in NYC than Starbuck's and McDonald's combined!

**3**

FALSE.
The Swiss eat more chocolate than any other nation. On average, each person east 8.8kg per year.

**4**

TRUE.
In 1904, Morrison (a dentist) and Wharton (a confectioner) took their 'fairy floss' to the St Louis World's Fair.

**5**

FALSE.
Beef tongue is a popular flavour in Tokyo, Japan.

**6**

TRUE.
These are commonly found at local fairs!

**7**

FALSE.
This is simply playground lore – while it can be difficult to digest and you shouldn't swallow gum, it doesn't linger in your body and gets pushed out like everything else!

**8**

TRUE.
This is very popular in Singapore.

**9**

FALSE.
Technically white chocolate isn't chocolate at all; milk and dark chocolate are made from cocoa powder and white chocolate is made from cocoa butter. Because white chocolate isn't made from chocolate solids, it doesn't qualify as real chocolate.

**10**

FALSE.
This is commonly believed, but also incorrect – It is thought to derive from Italian use for something elite, because the king had 99 guards.

**11**

TRUE.
The sweets are produced in factories all over the world to accommodate every country's sweet needs!

**12**

TRUE.
This was done to commemorate the end of World War I.

**13**

FALSE.
While the name might suggest it, these sweets do not contain any alcohol.

**14**

TRUE.
The chocolate bar was released in 1930 by Frank and Ethel Mars. Unfortunately, the horse died two months before the couple released the chocolate bar.

**15**

TRUE.
The lollypop was certified in 2012, and weighed 3,176.5 kg. It was about as tall as a giraffe!

# PASTA AND PIZZA

**1**

**What is the singular word for spaghetti?**

a. Spaghetti
b. Spaghetto
c. Spaghetta

**2**

**Which country is known to deep-fry pizza?**

a. Scotland
b. Denmark
c. Italy

**3**

**How did people knead pasta before it was done by machinery?**

a. By foot
b. By fist
c. By elbow

**4**

**What year was the 'Hawaiian pizza' invented?**

a. 1922
b. 1942
c. 1962

**5**

**Which topping could you add to a pizza to make it spicy?**

a. Anchovies
b. Jalapeños
c. Olives

**6**

**What year was the first online pizza order made?**

a. 1994
b. 1999
c. 2003

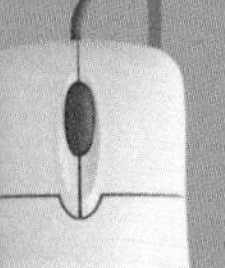

**7**

**What weight is a typical portion of pasta?**

a. 300 g
b. 150 g
c. 75 g

**8**

**What percentage of Brits do you think like pineapple on pizza?**

a. 78%
b. 53%
c. 20%

**9**

**What is farfalle pasta shaped like?**

a. Butterflies
b. Pyramids
c. Spirals

**10**

**What organisation funded research that resulted in a 3D printer for pizza?**

a. Tesla
b. NASA
c. Apple

# PASTA AND PIZZA

**1**

**b. Spaghetto.**

Spaghetti is actually the plural noun and an individual strand of the noodle-like pasta is called spaghetto.

**2**

**a. Scotland.**

Some Scottish establishments have been known to also deep-fry chocolate confectionary.

**3**

**a. By foot.**

While it was done by hand in most people's homes, in factories where they were making large quantities they would mix and knead with their feet while sitting on benches.

**4**

**c. 1962.**

The pizza was created in Canada by Greek native, Sam Panopoulos.

**5**

**b. Jalapeños.**

Jalapeños are a type of chili pepper and can be used to spice up a pizza.

**6**

**a. 1994.**

The order was placed with Pizza Hut.

**7**

**c. 75g.**

Packets in the UK usually suggest 75g. This may not be what you want to hear, but the smaller portion size is recommended.

**8**

**b. 53%.**

A survey in 2017 found that 84% of Brits like pizza, 82% like pineapple but only 53% would put them together and enjoy it!

**9**

**a. Butterflies.**

Farfalle is the Italian word for butterfly.

**10**

**b. NASA.**

NASA wanted astronauts to be able to create fresh meals on space missions. BeeHex used concepts developed by the grant to build a robot that can make pizza.

# AGRICULTURE

TRUE or FALSE

1

Agriculture is the single largest type of employment in the world.

2

72% of all the land in the UK is used for agriculture.

3

The UK produces around 25% of the food it consumes.

4

For every £1 invested in agriculture in th UK, £7.40 is delivered back to the economy.

5

Agriculture provides 100,000 jobs in the UK.

6

Globally, around 10% of human-edible crops are fed to animals.

7

40% of all food grown in the US is never eaten.

**8**

Agriculture is responsible for 10% of greenhouse gas emissions.

**9**

Agriculture accounts for 70% of freshwater use.

**10**

Chinese agriculture is a small but growing sector in the Chinese economy.

**11**

66% of the population in Nepal is directly engaged in farming.

**12**

Greece has a global reputation for exporting olives.

**13**

India is the largest fruit producer in the world.

**14**

Spain produces more olive oil than Italy.

**15**

Most of the world's farms are owned by corporate companies.

# AGRICULTURE

TRUE or FALSE

**1**

FALSE.
Agriculture makes up around 27% of global employment, second to the service sector at roughly 50%.

**2**

TRUE.
This statistic excludes woodland. The agricultural area is around 17.6 million hectares, with an additional 3.2 million hectares covered by woodland and forests.

**3**

FALSE.
Although the UK imports lots of produce from abroad, it produces around 50% of the nation's food on home soil.

**4**

TRUE.
The British countryside brings over £21 billion in tourism from all over the world.

**5**

FALSE.
It actually provides around 500,000 jobs (including supporting jobs through procurement activity that benefits other UK sectors like transport and construction).

**6**

False.
The figure is around 34%. The food is fed to animals for meat and dairy production.

**7**

TRUE.
This is unfortunately true at a time when one in eight families in the US struggle to put food on the table.

# QUIZ 66 ANSWERS

**8**

FALSE.
It is unfortunately a higher percentage – sitting at around 25%.

**9**

TRUE.
By 2050, agriculture will need to be increased by 60% in order to feed an estimated 9 billion people, resulting in even more need for water withdrawals.

**10**

FALSE.
It is one of the most important economic sectors of China, employing over 300 million farmers. It primarily produces rice and ranks first in the world for output.

**11**

TRUE.
Nepal has a broad variety of of food crops and livestock. Livestock products are sold for cash and are one of the most important sources of income for farming households.

**12**

TRUE.
The olives are often made into olive oil. Greece is also a main EU producer of cheese, yoghurt and cotton.

**13**

FALSE.
It is the second largest fruit producer in the world. China tops the list!

**14**

TRUE.
It produces around 40% of the world's olive oil, and produces more than three times as much as Italy, Greece or Tunisia.

**15**

FALSE.
It is estimated that over 90% of the world's farms are owned by families or individuals.

# NATIONAL DISHES

**1** **Which African country's national dish is jollof rice?**
a. Nigeria b. Egypt c. Mozambique

**2** **What is the United States' national food?**
a. Pizza b. Hamburger c. Pretzel

**3** **Goulash is the national dish of where?**
a. Hungary b. Poland c. United Kingdom

**4** **Which of these is a national dish of England?**
a. Roast beef and yorkshire pudding
b. Cheese and pickle sandwich
c. Cornish pasty

**5** **Where is wiener schnitzel the national dish?**
a. Germany b. Netherlands c. Austria

**6** **What is the national dish of France?**
a. Crêpe b. Soufflé c. Pot-au-feu

**7** **Where is kibbeh the national dish?**
a. Spain b. Syria c. Switzerland

**8** **What is the national dish of Ireland?**
a. Stew b. Haggis c. Sausage roll

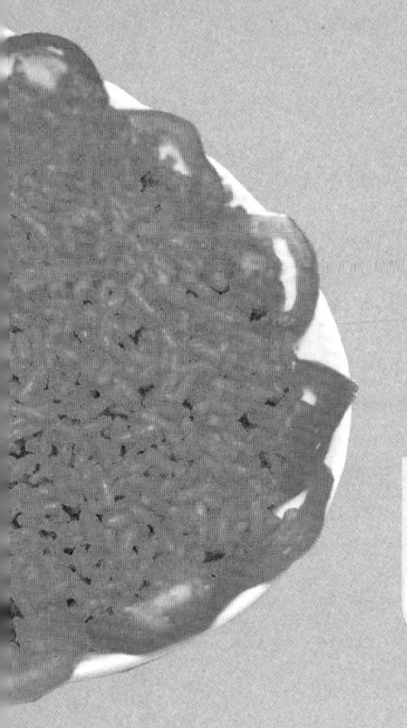

**9** **Bulgogi is the national dish of where?**
a. Australia b. South Korea c. New Zealand

**10** **What is the national dish in Barbados?**
a. Cou-cou and flying fish
b. Lamb tagine
c. Quinoa

**11** **Greenland's national dish is called Hákarl, do you know what it is?**
a. Whale b. Dolphin c. Shark

**12** **What is the national dish of Costa Rica?**
a. Gallo pinto b. Spanish omelette c. Frittata

**13** **Which European country's national dishes include moussaka and fasolada?**
a. Ukraine b. Greece c. Lithuania

**14** **What is South Africa's national dish?**
a. Cottage pie b. Bobotie c. Chicken tikka massala

**15** **Meat pie is the national dish of where?**
a. Thailand b. Australia c. New Zealand

# NATIONAL DISHES

**1** **a. Nigeria.** Jollof rice is popular across many west African countries. It is made using rice, tomatoes, peppers, tomato paste, chillis, onions and spices.

**2** **b. Hamburgers.** There is no argument that hamburgers are one of the most popular dishes in the US. Louis' Lunch in Connecticut has been serving them since 1900 and claims to be the oldest hamburger restaurant in the US.

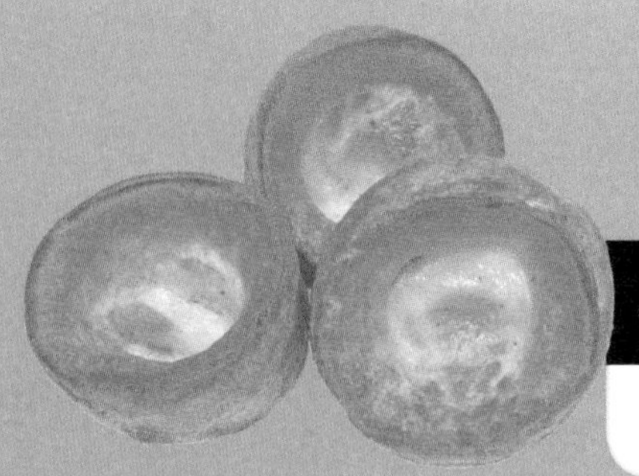

**3** **a. Hungary.** This is a filling stew consisting of beef, vegetables and spices and became the national dish in the late 1800s.

**4** **a. Roast beef and yorkshire pudding.** Can't go too far wrong with a traditional Sunday lunch! Yorkshire puddings were originally served as fillers before the main course for those who couldn't afford much beef.

**5** **c. Austria.** This is traditionally eaten with parsley and lemon slices alongside potato salad.

**6** **c. Pot-au-feu.** Translated this means pot-in-the-fire. It is a rustic dish consisting of steak, root vegetables and spices. Cooks will often sieve the broth and serve it separately from the meat.

**7** **b. Syria.** This concoction is made up of ground lamb, bulgur and lots of spices!

**8** **a. Stew.** This was originally a thick broth of slow-boiled mutton with onions, potatoes and parsley; nowadays, other vegetables like carrots have been incorporated.

**9** **b. South Korea .**This meal consists of grilled, thinly sliced cuts of meat marinated in soy sauce, sesame oil, garlic, onions, ginger, sugar and rice wine.

**10** **a. Cou-cou and flying fish.** Cou-cou is a polenta-like cornmeal cooked with okra that happens to go perfectly with flying fish that is steamed in lime juice and spices!

**11** **c. Shark .**The meat is cured with a fermentation process and left out to dry for five months!

**12** **a. Gallo pinto.** This is basically rice and beans, with some nice garnish! It may sound boring, but tastes great and you can make it your own by adding some sauces or meat.

**13** **b. Greece.** Moussaka is a layered casserole dish of meat and vegetables. Fasolada is a white bean soup.

**14** **b. Bobotie.** This popular dish consists of spiced minced meat that is baked with an egg-based topping!

**15** **b. Australia.** Australians love a fist-sized pie filled with ground meat and gravy. It is common to top the pie with tomato ketchup before eating.

# EXPENSIVE FOODS

### 1

**What is the most expensive spice in the world?**

a. Saffron
b. Turmeric
c. Cardamom

### 2

**How much is the most expensive burger in the world?**

a. $500
b. $5,000
c. $50

### 3

**Everyone loves a chocolate sundae, but what key ingredient do you think makes The Frrrozen Haute Chocolate ice cream sundae worth $25,000?**

a. Rubies b. Pearls
c. Diamonds

### 4

**How much is the most expensive pizza in the world?**

a. £9,000
b. £19,000
c. £29,000

### 5

**They may not look it, but white truffles are among the most expensive foods in the world. Roughly, how expensive do you think they are?**

a. €1,000 per kg
b. €10,000 per kg
c. €4,000 per kg

### 6

**Where in the world can you get a $66 pizza at Domino's?**

a. Japan
b. United States
c. Greece

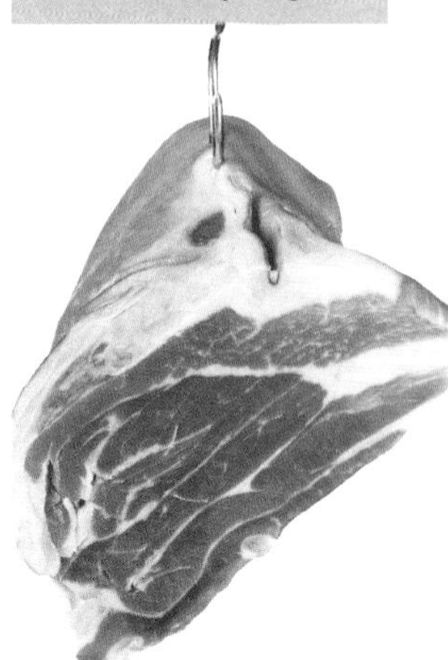

### 7

**Where can you find the finest Iberico ham?**

a. France and Italy
b. Spain and Portugal
c. Germany and Switzerland

## 8

**One of the most expensive coffees in the world is Kopi Luwak; but what is special about this bean?**

a. It is soaked in water for 30 days before being roasted
b. The beans have been vomited up by weasels
c. It consists of partially digested coffee beans that have been eaten and pooed out by civets

## 9

**How much is the most expensive caviar in the world?**

a. £20,000 per kg
b. £5,000 per kg
c. £15,000 per kg

## 10

**What is the most expensive cheese in the world?**

a. Pule
b. Halloumi
c. Cheddar

## 11

**What part of an animal is foie gras?**

a. Eyeball
b. Heart
c. Liver

## 12

**Where does the world's most expensive water come from?**

a. New Zealand
b. Hawaii
c. Spain

## 13

**Swallow's nest soup might sound gross, but it can cost a pretty penny! How much can it cost?**

a. £10 per bowl
b. £20 per bowl
c. £70 per bowl

## 14

**One kilogram of dry saffron needs at least how many flowers?**

a. 1,000
b. 10,000
c. 100,000

## 15

**Where does Elvish honey come from?**

a. Oman
b. Turkey
c. Mongolia

# EXPENSIVE FOODS

### 1

**a. Saffron.** Weight for weight this spice is more expensive than gold! It is so expensive because it is so labour-intensive to harvest.

### 2

**b. $5,000.** Consisting of wagyu beef, seared foie gras and black truffle shavings, this burger can be found in Las Vegas at the restaurant Fleur! The burger is served with a 25-year-old bottle of wine... which may account for a chunk of the cost too.

### 3

**c. Diamonds.** At the bottom of these ice creams you will find an 18-karat gold diamond bracelet.

### 4

**a. £9,000.** On this pizza you will find three of the rarest types of caviar, lobster from Norway and mozzarella. The only place you will find this pizza, however, is in Salerno, Italy.

### 5

**c. €4,000 per kg.** These truffles are found widely in Italy. Around the world they are commonly served with pasta or scrambled eggs.

### 6

**a. Japan.** The pizza doesn't have gold on it, but it does have Kobe beef, which is very expensive all over the world!

### 7

**b. Spain and Portugal.** The ham is cured for 36 months! In 2020 a leg of Iberico ham sold for almost £10,000 in Japan.

## 8

**c. It consists of partially digested coffee beans that have been eaten and pooed out by civets.** This originated in Indonesia, but is popular all over the world. In the UK it is sold for around £300 per kilogram.

## 9

**a. £20,000 per kg.** This is known as 'Almas' which is from the Iranian beluga sturgeon. It is produced from the eggs of a rare albino sturgeon.

## 10

**a. Pule.** This Serbian cheese is 60% Balkan donkey milk and 40% goat milk. It can be up to €1,000 per kg, and its rarity makes it so expensive.

## 11

**c. Liver.** It is the liver of a duck or goose that has been fattened. The food is banned in several countries due to its controversial treatment of the bird.

## 12

**b. Hawaii.** Kona Nigari water comes from deep under the ocean. The depth it is taken from supposedly means it is free from pollution and it is claimed to aid skin conditions.

## 13

**c. £70 per bowl.** The nests are hardened strands of the bird's saliva. They are usually white but they can come in a variety of colours!

## 14

**c. 100,000.** Each flower has only three threads. It flowers for only a week or so each year and must be harvested by hand in the morning when the flowers are closed.

## 15

**b. Turkey.** This is the world's most expensive honey and is sold at €5,000 per kg. It is harvested from hives in caves. It is claimed that the honey is high in minerals.

# FESTIVE FOODS

TRUE or FALSE

**1**

Eel is traditionally eaten in Italy on Christmas Eve.

**2**

Traditional mince pies are vegetarian.

**3**

Southern fried chicken is a popular Christmas meal in Japan.

**4**

Lithuanians celebrate Christmas by tucking into a Smörgåsbord containing 12 dishes.

**5**

Lutefisk is a cheese-based Christmas dish eaten in Norway.

**6**

Panettone is a festive sweet bread from France.

**7**

Stollen is a bread-like fruit cake from Germany.

**8**

Salted cod is a traditional Christmas meal in Mexico.

**9**

Hamburgers are the traditional Christmas food of Greenland.

**10**

Fish soup is traditionally served during Christmas dinner in Czechia.

**11**

In France, people like to eat oysters during the festive season.

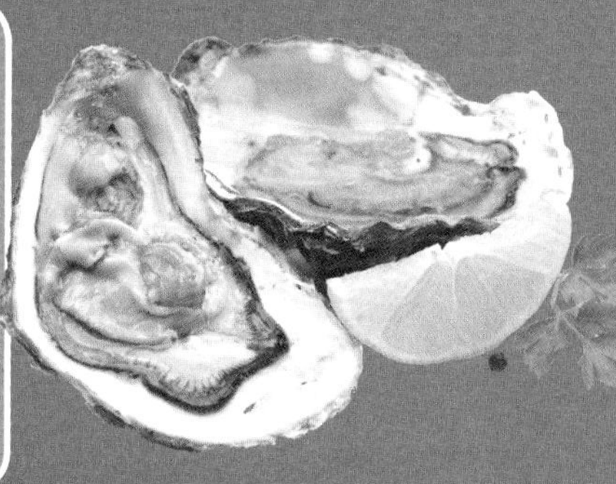

**12**

Many Australians choose to have a BBQ for Christmas dinner.

**13**

Christmas pudding is often soaked in alcohol and set on fire in the United Kingdom.

**14**

In the Philippines, a sweet and sticky yellow rice is eaten on Christmas Day.

# FESTIVE FOODS

TRUE or FALSE

**1**

TRUE.
Eel is very popular along the Amalfi Coast during the winter, making them a staple at Christmas time.

**2**

FALSE.
Traditional mince pies used suet (animal fat) in the recipe but nowadays many vegetarian and vegan alternatives can be found.

**3**

TRUE.
Marketing for southern fried chicken was so successful that it has become a Christmas tradition!

**4**

TRUE.
Each dish stands for one of the apostles. In Lithuania, as part of their holiday fasting the meal will not have any meat, egg or dairy products.

**5**

FALSE.
It is a dried or salted whitefish (commonly cod).

**6**

FALSE.
Panettone is a sweet bread from northern Italy but is enjoyed around the world.

**7**

TRUE.
The cake originated in the city of Dresden.

**8**

TRUE.
Like Norwegians, Mexicans also enjoy salted fish, but this dish is much more spicy!